P9-CDP-678

When Is A 'Flower' Not A Flower?

and other intriguing questions about plants

Larry & Carol Peterson

Designed by Forrest Phillips
Cover photos by Terry Marklevitz

©2014 Larry & Carol Peterson

All rights reserved. No part of this publication may be reproduced, distributed, or transmitted in any form or by any means, including photocopying, recording, or other electronic or mechanical methods, without the prior written permission of the publisher, except in the case of brief quotations embodied in critical reviews.

Printed in Canada

ISBN 978-0-9939750-0-4

FIN 13 11 2014

To order additional copies visit www.volumesdirect.com

Library and Archives Canada Cataloguing in Publication

Peterson, R. Larry, author
      When is a flower not a flower? / Larry & Carol Peterson.
ISBN 978-0-9939750-0-4 (pbk.)

      1. Plants--Miscellanea. 2. Plants--Pictorial works.
I. Peterson, Carol A., author II. Title.

QK50.P472014   581   C2014-907766-1

Online ordering also available at
www.petersonbook.com

For our sons, Ryan and Christopher, and our granddaughter, Miranda.
They have enriched our lives.

TABLE OF CONTENTS

Preface

Introduction

I. Food from plants

A. Seeds

B. Stems and Leaves

C. Roots

D. Fruits

II. Trees

III. Leaves

IV. Flowers

V. Roots

VI. Some commercial products from plants

VII. Plants as sources of medicine

VIII. Miscellaneous questions

Appendix 1

Methods used in obtaining images

Appendix 2

Common and scientific names of plants

Glossary

Preface

Plants are all around us. We depend on them for food and many medicinal compounds; we use them to make much of our clothing; we enhance our living space with their foliage and flowers; we cut up their wood and use it for building, making paper, and providing heat. Plants are so common that we rarely stop to think of how integral they are to our lives. Unfortunately plants are often considered to be simple, rather dull organisms. As we illustrate with this book, however, they are actually highly complex and fascinating living organisms.

This unique book takes common observations of plants and presents scientific explanations for them that the non-specialist can understand. The book also extends a view of plants into the microscopic world.

About the Authors

Larry and **Carol Peterson** were born in Alberta, Canada, and received degrees in botany from the University of Alberta and the University of California, Davis. Both had teaching and research careers in Ontario, Canada, Larry at the University of Guelph and Carol at the University of Waterloo.

Now retired, they continue to publish research papers, book chapters, and DVDs. They collaborated on the book "**Teaching Plant Structure Through Creative Laboratory Exercises**" for which they were awarded the Lawson Medal from the Canadian Botanical Association for an outstanding contribution to the field of botany.

Acknowledgements

We thank **Canadian Science Publishing** (formerly NRC Research Press) for permission to use some of our previously published images in two books and two DVDs. We also thank several individuals, acknowledged in the text, for providing images. Most of the diagrams are by Ishari Waduwara-Jayabahu; we thank her for the care in preparing these. We are especially grateful for the very helpful comments made by Pei-Chun Chang, Linda Evers, Hannah Fournier, Christopher Peterson, and Ryan Peterson. We also thank Carole Ann Lacroix, Lewis Melville, Chris Meyer, Sandy Smith, and Kevin Stevens for help in obtaining some of the images. We are indebted to Chris Meyer for his thorough editing, and to Forrest Phillips for his skill in designing the book and for his many suggestions that improved the final copy.

Selected References

Benzing, D.H. 2012. **Air Plants. Epiphytes and Aerial Gardens.** Cornell University Press. New York.

Dickison, W.C. 2000. **Integrative Plant Anatomy**. Academic Press. San Diego.

Evert, R.F. and Eichhorn, S.E. 2013. **Biology of Plants. 8th Edition**. W.H. Freeman and Company. New York.

Kershaw, L. 2001. **Trees of Ontario**. Lone Pine Publishing. Edmonton.

Levetin, E. and McMahon, K. 2011. **Plants and Society**. 6th Edition Wm. C. Brown Publishers. Dubuque.

Peterson, R.L., Peterson, C.A. and Melville, L.H. 2008. **Teaching Plant Anatomy Through Creative Laboratory Exercises**. NRC Press. Ottawa.

Sandved, K.B. 1993. **Bark**. Timber Press, Portland Oregon.

Simpson, B.B. and Ogorzally, M. C. 2013. **Economic Botany: Plants in Our World 4th Edition**. McGraw-Hill, Inc. New York.

Small, E. and Catling, P.M. 1999. **Canadian Medicinal Crops**. NRC Press. Ottawa.

Turner, N.J. and von Aderkas, P. 2009. **The North American Guide to Common Poisonous Plants and Mushrooms**. Timber Press. Portland. London.

Introduction

This book is organized around a series of questions about plants. Although the majority of questions come from our own experience as botanists, some have been suggested by friends and acquaintances. A few questions will be easily answered by most readers and although others appear simple, the reader may be surprised by the answers. Many questions are linked to human-plant interactions while others deal with the 'nuisance factor' of some plants. The answers, illustrated with images, do not require a scientific background to be understood. Specialized terms are kept to a minimum and, when used, they appear **bold** in the text and are defined in a **Glossary**.

Many questions deal with specific plant parts as well as plant cells. The basic structures and terms for these are illustrated in the diagrams below.

Plant parts

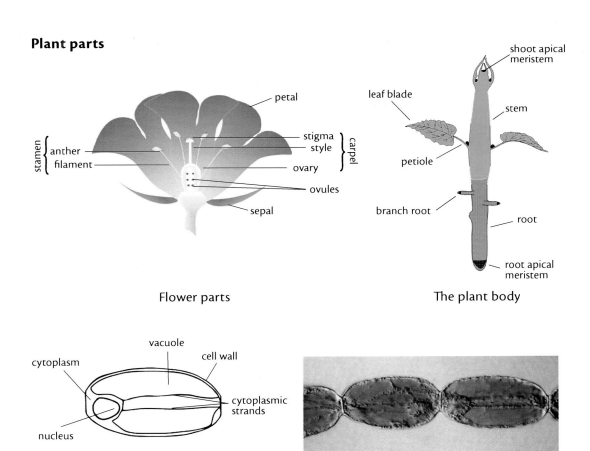

Flower parts

The plant body

An example of a plant cell

11

Methods used in obtaining images

Although numerous images used in the answers to questions were taken with digital cameras, others have required the use of different types of microscopes interfaced with cameras. For many of the latter images, plant parts were prepared by various methods before microscopic examination. Brief descriptions of these methods (found in **Appendix 1**) provide a more in-depth understanding of the images used.

Common names of most plants are used throughout the book and corresponding scientific names are given in **Appendix 2**.

Century Plant (Photo by Forrest Phillips)

I. FOOD FROM PLANTS

I. Food from plants

A. Seeds

What is a seed?

A seed is an embryonic plant along with a supply of stored food encased in a **seed coat**. The seed coat prevents water loss and the invasion by fungi and other organisms that would lead to spoilage. There are huge variations in size, colour, and structure of seeds. Mature seeds enter a period of **dormancy**. Most seeds are designed to withstand unfavorable conditions such as extreme temperatures, and lack of water.

Tomato seeds that had been coated with a fungicide to prevent spoilage by fungi

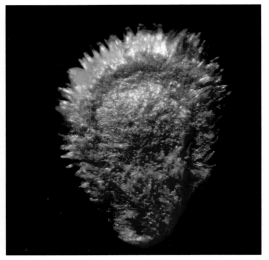

Higher magnification of a tomato seed

Barley seeds

Common garden bean seeds

When the seed coat is removed from a garden bean, the **embryo** is apparent. The two large structures are **cotyledons** that contain stored food that provides nutrients to the seedling during its initial stages of growth. The smaller part of the embryo (root and shoot) are dwarfed by the cotyledons. However, as the seedling develops after seed **germination**, the root and shoot grow at the expense of the cotyledons.

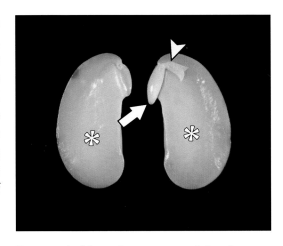

Bean seed with seed coat removed showing two cotyledons (✱) and an embryonic shoot (arrowhead) and root (arrow)

How do seeds develop?

Seeds develop as a result of sexual reproduction. A portion of the female part of the flower is the **ovary** and this contains **ovules**.

Following **pollination** and **fertilization** each ovule develops into a seed. The surrounding ovary tissue matures to form a **fruit**.

Hibiscus flower

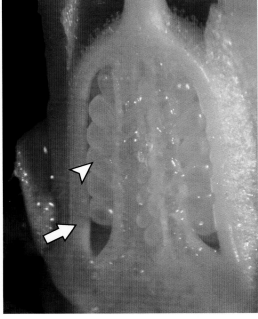

Ovary (arrow) of a *Hibiscus* flower cut open to show many ovules (arrowhead)

Why are seeds important sources of nutrition for humans?

During seed development, storage products are deposited for later use by the plant during **germination** and early seedling development. Among these storage products are **proteins**, **starch**, and **lipids**. These are important sources of nutrition for humans. The proportions of storage products and their locations in seeds depend on the species. In some cases food is stored in **cotyledons** while in others it is located in a separate region called the **endosperm**.

Various crops are grown that provide one or more of the storage products within their seeds. For example, sunflowers are grown primarily for the oil that can be extracted from their seeds although they do contain proteins as well.

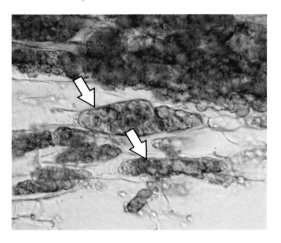

Sunflower seeds, some with seed coat removed

Stained oils (arrows) in cells of a sunflower seed

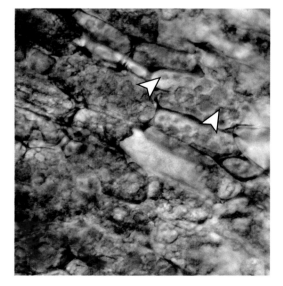

Seeds of many bean species, including garden beans, are rich in proteins but also contain a considerable amount of starch.

Stained proteins (arrowheads) in cells of a sunflower seed

Bean seed with seed coat removed and stained red for protein

16

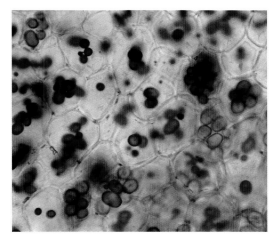

Stained starch grains within bean seed cells

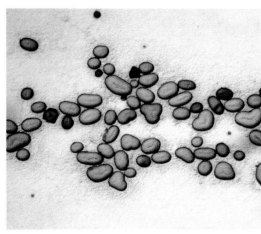

Stained starch grains extracted from a bean seed

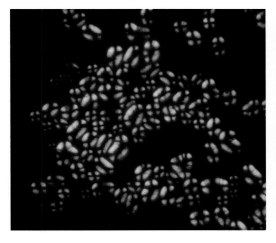

Starch grains extracted from a bean seed and viewed with polarized light showing the crystalline nature of starch

Corn kernels

Corn **kernels** (single seeded **fruits**) are a major source of calories for people and animals in many countries. These kernels store large quantities of starch in the endosperm, oil in the 'germ' (**embryo**), as well as smaller quantities of proteins, both in the endosperm and embryo. The commercial product corn oil is extracted from the embryo, whereas corn starch is obtained from the endosperm.

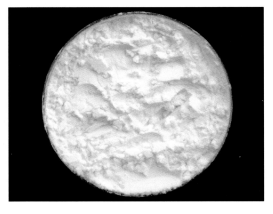

Corn starch, an important commercial product from corn kernels

  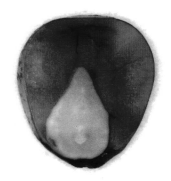

Sectioned corn kernel with starch (stained dark purple) in the endosperm; the white starch-free area is the embryo

Sectioned corn kernel with oils (stained red) concentrated in the embryo

Sectioned corn kernel with protein (stained purple) in the endosperm and embryo

Which seeds provide most of the protein in human diets?

Seeds of legumes (soybean, beans, lentils, chickpeas, peas, peanuts) provide much of the **proteins** for various cultures around the world.

Peanut seeds

Soybean plants with fruits   Soybean pod with seeds   Peanut fruits

 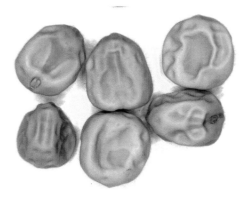

Red lentil seeds   Dry pea seeds

Which plants provide most of the calories in the human diet?

Of the six most important food crops, three are **cereals** (rice, wheat, corn or maize), one is a swollen, underground stem called a **tuber** (potato), and two are fleshy roots (sweet potato and cassava [manioc] from which tapioca is produced).

Rice growing in Thailand
(Photo by Christopher Peterson)

Rice at flowering stage

A bearded wheat variety

What is dietary fiber?

This material, essential for normal digestive function, is the **cellulose** from plant **cell walls**. Commercial bran, obtained from the outer covering of **cereal** grains, is particularly rich in dietary fiber.

Bran obtained from wheat

What parts of the coconut are used as food?

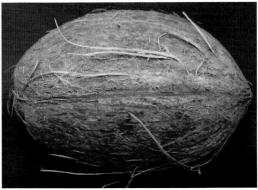

Solid white "meat" in coconut seed

A coconut is a fruit containing one very large seed which is the part used as a food source. The **embryo** within the seed is small and is surrounded by a large quantity of nutritive material (**endosperm**). Initially, the endosperm is liquid but during development some of it (adjacent to the seed coat) becomes solid, forming the white "meat" of the coconut. The endosperm in the center of the seed remains liquid. This liquid (coconut water) in green coconuts is used as a nutritious drink in many cultures.

Coconut fruits (Photo by Pei-Chun Chang)

Coconut seed

What is coconut milk?

Coconut milk, sold commercially, is derived from coconut meat that has been soaked in water and then squeezed to produce the liquid.

How do coconut seeds spread from island to island?

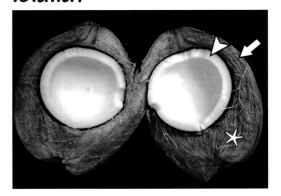

Coconut fruits can float and are dispersed by ocean currents. Each fruit is protected by a tough, waterproof, outer wall. Inside this is a fibrous layer that traps air, making the fruit buoyant. This layer encases one large seed. Coconut trees usually grow near shorelines and when the fruits are mature they often fall into the water.

Coconut fruit with outer waterproof layer (arrow), that has been split open to show the fibrous layer (✳) and a seed (arrowhead) (Photo by Dampiya Mahathanthila)

I. Food from plants

B. Stems and Leaves

What characteristics of potatoes make them an important staple food in many cultures?

The bulk of a potato **tuber** consists of cells that store large quantities of **starch**. They are also rich in vitamins, minerals, and a small amount of high quality **protein**.

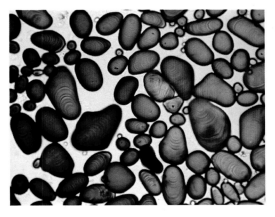

Stained starch grains from a potato tuber

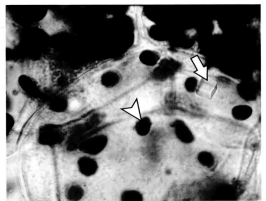

Stained starch (arrowhead) and a cube-shaped protein crystal (arrow) in potato tuber cells

Are potato tubers that turn green after exposure to light poisonous?

Light stimulates the synthesis of highly toxic substances such as solanine that, when ingested, can cause serious (but usually not fatal) health problems.

Potato tubers that have been exposed to light

How are potatoes propagated?

Potatoes are propagated vegetatively by cutting **tubers** into pieces making sure that at least one 'eye' (**dormant bud**) is present that will grow into a new plant.

Potato tuber pieces with 'eyes' (arrows)

Potato tuber with new shoots

Are sweet potatoes the same as yams?

Although both sweet potatoes and yams are fleshy storage organs, sweet potatoes are true roots whereas yams are **tubers** (underground stems). Sweet potatoes belong to the genus **Ipomoea** (a member of the morning glory family) while yams belong to the genus **Dioscorea** (a member of the Dioscoreaceae family).

Sweet potatoes

A variety of yams

What is a stalk of celery?

A celery stalk consists of a group of elongated **petioles** that support the **leaf blades**.

Celery stalk consisting of petioles (arrowheads) and leaf blades (✻)

What gets caught in your teeth when you eat celery?

The petioles of celery develop bundles of strengthening cells in ridges just under its surface for support – these bundles are the "strings" that get caught between teeth.

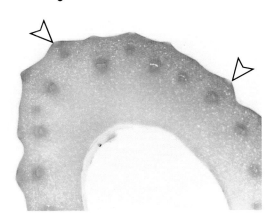

Sectioned celery petiole with ridges (arrowheads)

A group of stained strengthening cells (✻) in a ridge of a celery petiole

What are onion bulbs?

Onion bulbs consist of a short stem and closely packed, modified leaves. The fleshy structures that we eat are the swollen bases of the leaves.

Onion bulbs

Why do onions make us cry when they are cut?

Onion bulbs contain volatile sulfur compounds that are released from cells when they are cut. When these compounds contact the fluid on the surface of eyes, they form sulfuric acid that causes a burning sensation.

What are fiddleheads?

Fiddleheads that are safe to eat are the furled leaves of the Ostrich fern. Most fern species show this method of leaf development. However, only a few fern species are edible and some are, in fact, poisonous!

Furled leaf of **Polypodium crassifolium**

Harvested fiddleheads of the Ostrich fern (Photo by Dean Whittier)

I. Food from plants

C. Roots

Why are roots of garden beets red?

The red colour of garden beets is due to the presence of a pigment, **betacyanin**, located in their cells. When beets are cut before cooking some of the cells are injured, releasing pigments into the water.

Cut garden beet root

Betacyanins in cells of a beet root; the clear cells were injured and lost their betacyanins as the root was cut

What makes carrot roots orange?

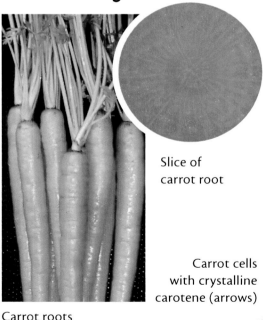

Cells of carrot roots have a type of **plastid** called a **chromoplast**. These special plastids contain crystalline **carotene** that is responsible for the carrot root's distinctive colour. Unlike most crystals, those of carotene are in the form of flat sheets that can take many shapes depending on whether they are lying flat, or are rolled or folded within the plastid.

Slice of carrot root

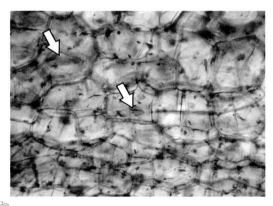

Carrot cells with crystalline carotene (arrows)

Carrot roots

Does eating carrots improve eyesight?

Carotene is a good source of vitamin A, a precursor of the pigment in the rod cells of eyes. Thus, eating carrots can improve night vision. However, they will not cure diseases of the eyes.

I. Food from plants

D. Fruits

Test yourself. Which of the following are fruits and which are vegetables?

Lettuce	Tomato	Corn	Cucumber
Raspberry	Grape	Cauliflower	Beet
Carrot	Beans	Celery	Apple
Cherry	Potato	Avocado	Banana
Pepper	Blueberry	Pineapple	Zucchini

What is the difference between a fruit and a vegetable?

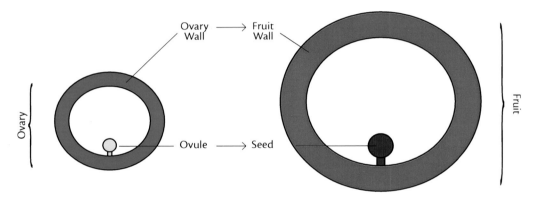

A vegetable is obtained from the vegetative (non-sexual) part of the plant. Vegetative parts are leaves, stems and roots. Some common vegetables are lettuce (leaves), asparagus (mainly stems) and carrots (roots). In contrast, a fruit is a product of the **ovary** of a flower and, in some cases, its closely associated parts. The wall of the ovary becomes the fruit wall, and fertilized **ovules** within the ovary become the seeds within the fruit. In corn and other grains, the seed wall fuses with the fruit wall during development so that at maturity, they appear to be one layer.

F	Zucchini	F	Pineapple	F	Blueberry	F	Pepper
F	Banana	F	Avocado	V	Potato	F	Cherry
F	Apple	V	Celery	F	Beans	V	Carrot
V	Beet	V	Cauliflower	F	Grape	F	Raspberry
F	Cucumber	F	Corn	F	Tomato	V	Lettuce

26

Why are beans, tomatoes, cucumbers, squash, corn, and peppers fruits?

Although all these are commonly referred to as vegetables, they are actually fruits because they develop from ovaries, and the seeds they contain have developed from fertilized ovules.

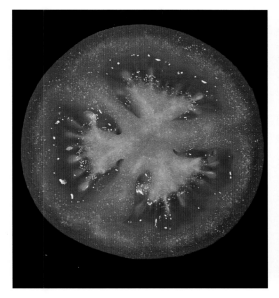

Seeds in a tomato fruit

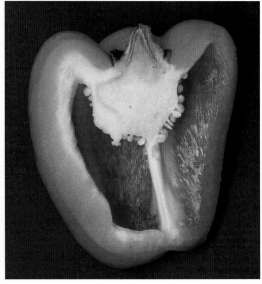

Seeds in a red pepper

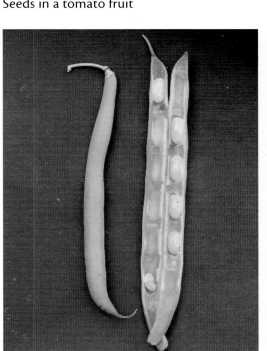

Seeds in a garden bean

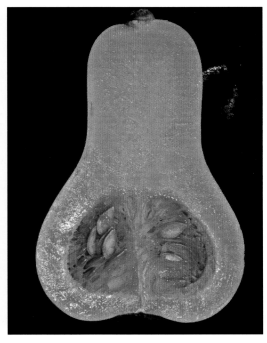

Seeds in a butternut squash
(Photo by Ishari Waduwara-Jayabahu)

What gives peppers their colours at maturity?

Immature pepper fruits are green due to the presence of numerous chloroplasts. Some pepper varieties remain green at maturity while others turn red, yellow or orange. In these cases **chlorophyll** within **chloroplasts** decreases and **carotenoid** pigments increase. The plastids are then referred to as **chromoplasts**.

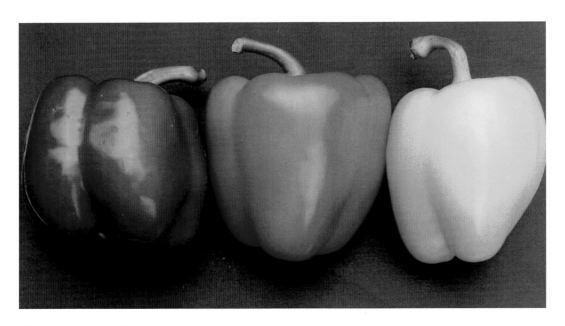

Green, red, and yellow peppers

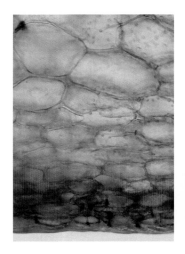
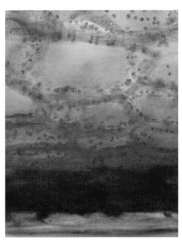
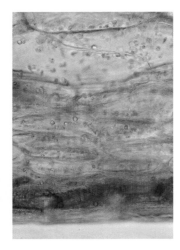

Green chloroplasts   Red chromoplasts   Yellow chromoplasts

How do tomatoes turn colour as they ripen?

The green colour of unripe tomatoes is due to chlorophyll found within chloroplasts. As these fruits ripen, chlorophyll levels fall and **carotenoids** such as **lycopene** increase. The chloroplasts, therefore, are converted into chromoplasts.

Green tomato

Partially ripened tomato

Fully ripened tomato

What produces the characteristic aroma when citrus fruits are peeled?

The peels of fruits such as oranges, limes, and lemons have many internal secretory structures called **glands** that produce aromatic oils. These accumulate in the hollow centers of the glands. When the fruit is peeled, some of these oils are released.

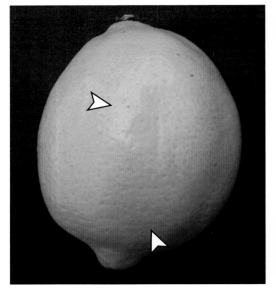

Lemon fruit showing indentations that indicate the locations of the glands (arrowheads)

Slice of lemon fruit showing oil glands just under the surface (arrowheads)

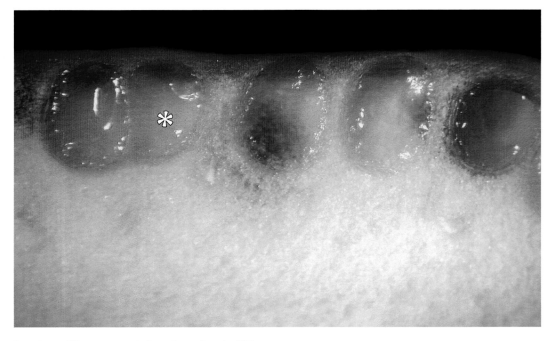

Section of lemon peel showing glands (✱)

How do you feel about eating fleshy hairs?

The structures in all citrus fruits that are commonly called juice sacs are actually enlarged **hairs**.

Inset - Individual hair that has been lifted from a segment

Orange segment from which the covering membrane was removed showing tightly packed, swollen hairs

Why does the flesh of an avocado feel slippery to the touch?

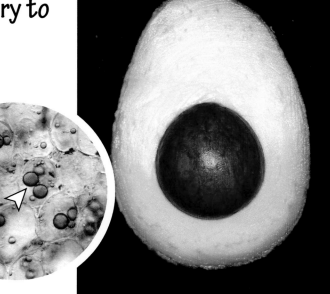

Avocadoes are fruits consisting of a stony pit (containing a seed) surrounded by cells with numerous oil bodies. The oil makes the flesh feel slippery.

Stained oils (arrowheads) in avocado fruit cells

Avocado fruit with pit

Why is it possible to 'polish' apples?

Apples have microscopic **wax** deposits that protrude from the surface. Rubbing an apple flattens this wax and gives the fruit its polished look.

Polished apple fruit

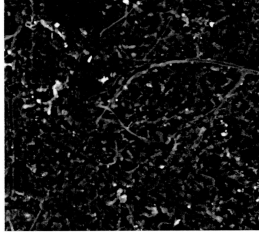

Waxy cuticle of apple fruit (SEM)

What makes pears 'gritty'?

The flesh of a pear consists mostly of thin-walled cells. However, groups of very thick-walled cells are also present. These are often referred to as '**stone cells**'. Their walls also contain **lignin** (a chemical that adds further strength to the walls) so they do not break down when chewed.

Pear fruit

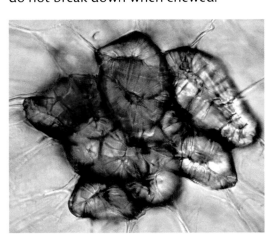

Stained stone cells in a pear fruit section

Which legume plants its own seeds?

The peanut, a member of the legume family, has a unique way of producing fruit. The plants have small flowers that can be either self- or bee-pollinated. Following fertilization, the base of the **ovary** elongates, forming a structure commonly called a peg (technically known as a gynophore). The developing fruit is located at the tip of this structure. The peg continues to elongate and grows towards the soil, eventually pushing the future fruit underground. Here the tip of the peg begins to swell and the **ovules** within it develop into seeds. As the seeds mature, they are protected by a papery seed coat and the fruit wall; the latter is often referred to as the shell. Even plants with mature fruit continue to flower and produce new pegs during the growing season. Because their fruits develop and mature underground, peanuts are often called groundnuts. However, both "peanuts" and "groundnuts" are misnomers because the fruits are legumes, not nuts.

Peanut plants on Kernal Farm, Vittoria Ontario

Peanut plant with maturing fruits

Peanut flower

Early stages in peg formation (arrowheads)

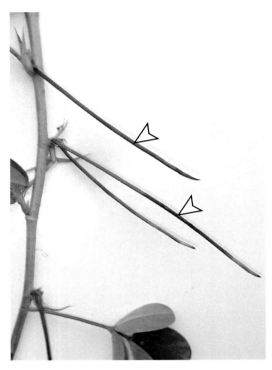

Elongated pegs (arrowheads)

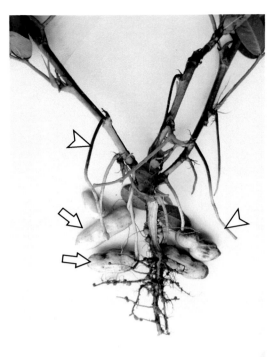

Pegs (arrowheads) and fruits (arrows)

Development of fruits at tips of pegs

II. TREES

II. Trees

How do trees become so tall?

A plant stem grows in length by the addition of new cells at its tip. These cells are produced by divisions that occur in a small group of cells known as an **apical meristem**. In trees, new cells are added over a number of years.

Tall hardwood trees with fall colours

How do the trunks of many trees become so wide?

Trees grow in width through the activity of two meristems (dividing cells), the **vascular cambium** and the **cork cambium**. The vascular cambium is responsible for most of the increase in width. It produces additional **wood** toward the inside of the stem, and sugar-conducting cells toward the outside. This process continues throughout the life of the tree.

Diagram illustrating the structure of a cross section of a two-year old tree trunk.

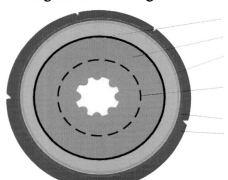

1. Vascular cambium
2. Wood cells produced by the vascular cambium
3. Sugar-conducting cells produced by the vascular cambium
4. Margin of an annual ring at end of first year's growth
5. Cork cambium
6. Cells produced by the cork cambium

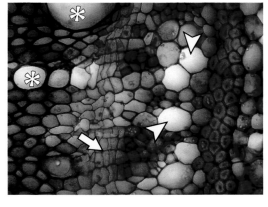

Cross section of stem showing vascular cambium (arrow) with new wood cells (✱) and sugar-conducting cells (arrowheads)

Red tingle *Eucalyptus* species in South Western Australia

Redwood tree in California, USA

How do trees make annual rings?

Stump of maple tree with annual rings

The activity of the **vascular cambium** and the size of the cells it produces vary during the year. In spring, the cells of the cambium divide rapidly and the **wood** cells it produces have large diameters. However, in the late fall, the cambium divides more slowly and the cells produced are much smaller. The greater density of the cell walls in the latter part of the wood give it a darker appearance, marking the edge of an **annual ring**.

Annual rings in a stained cross section of pawpaw stem

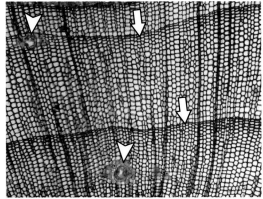

Stained cross section of pine wood showing small diameter cells formed at the end of two season's growth (arrows). Two resin ducts (arrowheads) are present

How can the age of a tree be determined?

The age of trees can be determined by counting the number of annual rings either in a cross section of a tree trunk or in a core taken through the diameter of the trunk. The science of aging trees through counting **annual rings** is called dendrochronology.

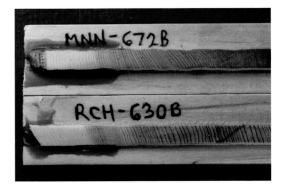

Cores taken from ancient eastern white cedar trees located on the Niagara Escarpment, Ontario. The distance between two dark lines indicates one year's growth. (Photo by Peter Kelly)

What is the difference between sapwood and heartwood?

The lighter outer part of the **wood** of a tree trunk is the **sapwood** that conducts the water and minerals (absorbed by the roots) to the leaves. The darker inner part is the **heartwood** that does not conduct water and minerals but continues to function in supporting the tree. It is dark in colour because of the deposition of **condensed tannins**, **resins**, and other organic compounds that have antimicrobial properties.

Sapwood and heartwood in red cedar tree

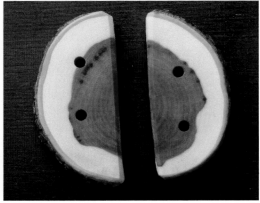

Sapwood and heartwood in buttons made from lilac

What is ebony?

Ebony is a very dark, dense **wood** used for such items as small carvings, furniture, the black keys of pianos, and guitar picks. It comes from the **heartwood** of several species in the tropical tree genus **Diospyros**.

Cross-section of an ebony log
(State Timber Corporation)

What is the difference between softwoods and hardwoods?

The terms often do not reflect the 'hardness' of the wood but rather are based on structural differences. Wood from conifers is termed **softwood** because it lacks **fibers**, and the water-conducting elements are all one primitive type. Wood from broad leaved trees is termed **hardwood**. It typically consists of many fibers, and two types of water-conducting cells, one primitive and one advanced (with wider diameters).

Stained cross section of pine (softwood) with primitive, narrow-diameter water-conducting cells and two resin ducts (✱)

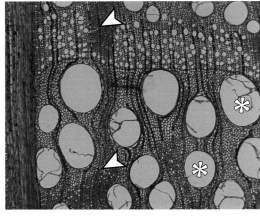

Stained cross section of oak (hardwood) with some advanced, large-diameter water-conducting cells (✱) and many, thick-walled, narrow-diameter fibers (arrowheads)

Why do trees make bark?

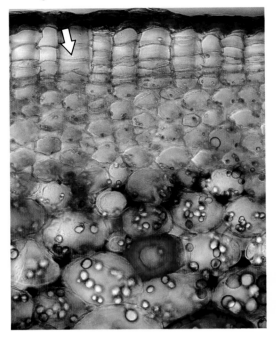

Dead air-filled cork cells (arrow)

The outer part of the **bark** protects plants from losing water and also prevents the entry of harmful organisms. This part of the bark consists of **cork** cells that die after depositing fatty substances (**suberin** and **wax**) in their walls. Some cork cells also deposit **condensed tannins** as they die, and these may also aid in preventing invasion by pathogens. Mature cork cells are filled with air.

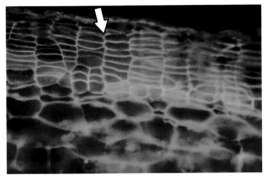

Suberized cork cells (arrow) viewed with UV light

Why is the bark of most trees cracked?

Cracked bark of a pine species

Trees expand in girth due to the activities of the **vascular cambium** and, to a lesser extent, the **cork cambium**. Most of the increase in diameter results from wood formed by the vascular cambium. The mature cells of the **outer bark** are dead and their walls cannot stretch. The pressure from inside the tree as it expands causes the outer layers of this tissue to crack.

Rough bark of black cherry

Why is birch bark white?

The **cork** cells of birch lack the brown-coloured condensed **tannins** that are usually found in cork cells. They are air-filled and reflect light. The horizontal lines visible on the surface of the **bark** are called **lenticels** and these consist of loosely arranged cells. These allow an exchange of gases to occur between the atmosphere and the underlying living cells of the tree trunk. Lenticels are obvious on trees that have smooth bark.

Lenticels (arrows) in bark of white birch

Why did indigenous North Americans use birch bark to construct their canoes?

Birch trees form a new cork cambium, and a complete cylinder of **cork** each year. This feature allowed large, intact pieces of **bark** to be removed from the tree trunk. Such bark pieces were sewn together with split tree roots, and sealed with **resin** from black or white spruce mixed with bear fat and charcoal. Birch-bark canoes were waterproof and light to carry on portages.

Peeling bark on yellow birch

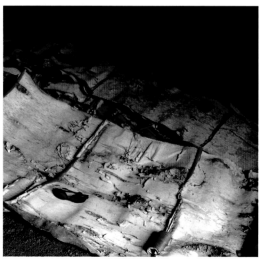

Large pieces of bark stripped from a yellow birch tree (note size in comparison with sunglasses)

What is the source of cork used in wine bottles?

Cork is obtained from the outer protective tissue of cork oak trees that are grown for this purpose. Because of their unusually thick cork, it can be stripped and then allowed to regenerate for subsequent harvests. Plantations of cork oak trees can be found, for example, in Spain and Portugal.

Bark on cork oak trees

What features of cork tissue make it suitable for bottle stoppers?

Cork cells are tightly packed together, dead at maturity, and are filled with air. The **suberin** and wax in the cell walls prevent the tissue from becoming waterlogged and also resist microbial invasion. The lack of **lignin** in the cell walls and the presence of air in the cavity of the cells allow cork to deform when pressed into a bottle.

Typical wine bottle cork

Cork is important historically. The first description of plant cells was based on observations of sections of a wine bottle cork by Robert Hooke in the seventeenth century.

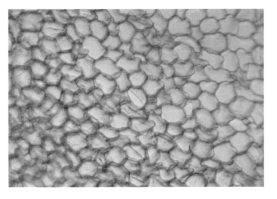

Cells in a section of a wine bottle cork

What are the squiggly lines that are often present beneath the bark of many trees?

Many insects, including bark beetles, can burrow into the thin-walled cells of the inner **bark** forming what are referred to as galleries.

Insect galleries in dead maple tree from which the outer bark has been shed

Where are resins produced in pines and other conifers, and what role do resins play?

Resins are formed in long, hollow structures called **resin ducts**. Cells lining the ducts secrete the resin into the cavity. Resin ducts develop throughout the plant, and the resin produced protects trees from harmful fungi and insects such as bark beetles. When the plant is injured, resin flows out of the ducts and hardens over the injured area protecting the plant from microbial attack.

Resin flow in white pine after branch removal

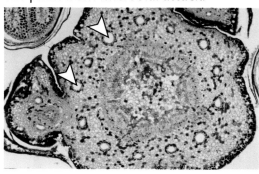

Stained cross section of pine stem with resin ducts (arrowheads)

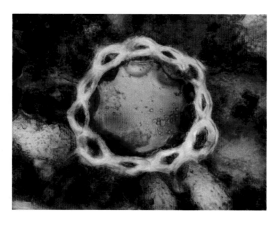

Cross section of a resin duct in a pine needle filled with red-stained resin

What is amber?

Amber is fossilized **resin** that often contains remains of insects and plant parts that fell into it while it was still sticky. Resin, and therefore the organisms trapped within, may be millions of years old. Amber is often used in making jewellery.

Fossil flower of
Protium coronatum in amber
(Photo by George Poinar)

What are the black swellings that sometimes occur on stems of plum and cherry trees?

These structures, called black knot, are formed by a fungus (***Apiosporina morbosa***). Spores that can infect plum or cherry trees in the vicinity are released from these structures. Heavy infestations can cause severe losses in fruit production.

Black knot disease on heavily infected ornamental plum tree

Why is it easy to separate the bark from the wood, especially in the spring?

The vascular cambium is dividing rapidly in the spring and the new cells produced have very thin walls that break easily.

Separation of bark from wood during spring growth of willow

III. LEAVES

III. Leaves

What causes the white patches on the leaves of many species?

The white regions are due to cells that lack **chloroplasts**. Instead they have a type of **plastid** known as a **leucoplast** that lacks **chlorophyll** and is, therefore, colourless.

Leaves of a **Hosta** species

Leaves of emerald gaiety **Euonymus**

What is responsible for the various colours of prayer plant leaves?

This leaf is unusual in that it has three distinct colours. The epidermal cells of the midrib (central vein) and major veins lack chlorophyll and have **anthocyanin** in their **vacuoles**, resulting in a bright red colour. Most of the interior cells of the **leaf blade** have chlorophyll. The lack of anthocyanin in the epidermal cells near the midrib and margins results in the grass-green areas. The deeper green areas result from a combination of chlorophyll in the inner cells along with anthocyanins in most of the upper and lower epidermal cells.

Prayer plant leaves

Why are the leaves of Japanese maples and barberrys not green?

The leaves of these plants have various colours because they contain large amounts of the pigment **anthocyanin** that mask the green colour of **chlorophyll**. Anthocyanin protects plants against too much UV radiation that could damage their DNA.

Leaves of Japanese maple

Leaves of barberry

What is responsible for the change in leaf colour in the fall?

Shortening day lengths and lowering temperatures induce changes in leaf colour. The showy reds and yellow/oranges of leaves of many trees in the fall are partly due to the degradation of **chlorophyll** responsible for the natural green colour. In leaves that turn red, as the chlorophyll levels fall, **anthocyanins** are produced. In leaves that become yellow/orange, the loss of chlorophyll unmasks existing **carotenoid** pigments.

Sugar maple leaves

Maple leaves losing chlorophyll and forming anthocyanins

Tulip tree leaves

Burning bush leaves

How do leaves exchange gases with the environment?

Leaves possess numerous **stomata** in their **epidermis**. These form when some epidermal cells become specialized as **guard cells**. Such cells occur in pairs in the epidermis of leaves and also young stems. Unlike the surrounding epidermal cells, they possess **chloroplasts**. Changes in the shape of the guard cells can result in an opening (a pore) between them. When a pore is present, gas exchange between the plant and atmosphere occurs. During **photosynthesis**, carbon dioxide from the air enters the leaf through the pores, and the oxygen released as a byproduct diffuses out into the atmosphere.

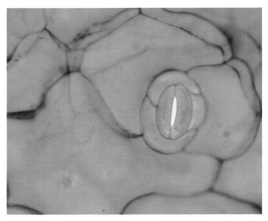
Stomate with an open pore in a **Kalanchoe** leaf

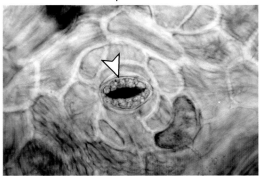
Guard cells with chloroplasts (arrowhead) in **Bryophyllum** leaf

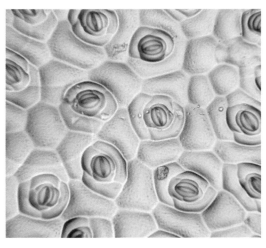
Impression of stomata in a **Kalanchoe** leaf obtained by painting the surface of the leaf with clear nail polish, letting it dry and then peeling it off.

How are leaves protected from losing too much water?

A surface view of a leaf shows that epidermal cells are tightly packed together, in some cases like pieces of a jigsaw puzzle. All epidermal cells have an external covering called a **cuticle** that is composed of **cutin** and **waxes**. These are water-proofing substances that prevent water loss and help to defend plants against pathogens and insects. The thickness of the cuticle varies depending on the environment in which the plant is growing. Plants adapted to dry conditions often have a very thick cuticle.

Pores between guard cells typically open during the day to maximize gas exchange for **photosynthesis**. During the night the pores close to reduce water loss. However, under conditions of drought, a stress **hormone** is produced that causes the pores to close even during the day.

Jigsaw-shaped epidermal cells (some with **anthocyanin** pigment) and guard cells (arrowheads) in velvet plant leaf

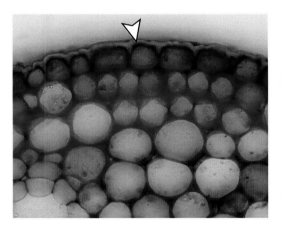

Blue-stained cuticle (arrowhead) on a cross section of an umbrella tree leaf

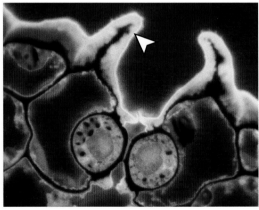

Thick cuticle (arrowhead) on stained cross section of a *Haworthia* leaf

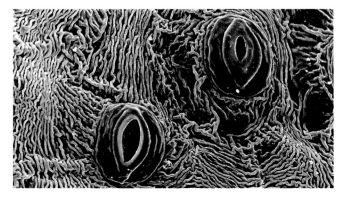

Ridged cuticle and open pores between guard cells on snapdragon leaf (SEM)

What makes the leaves of some plants feel 'fuzzy'?

Hairs, which may be just visible to the naked eye, cover the surfaces of these leaves. The hairs play several roles including the reduction of water loss, deflection of UV light, and prevention of insect attack. Each hair begins as an extension of an individual epidermal cell but it can continue to divide to form either unbranched or branched hairs. Many hairs achieve varied and beautiful shapes.

Fuzzy leaves of common mullein

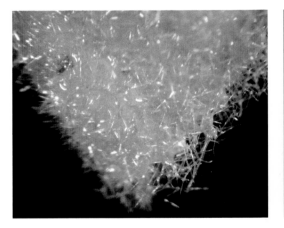

Branched hairs of common mullein (observed with deflected light on a dissecting microscope)

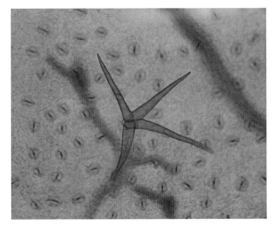
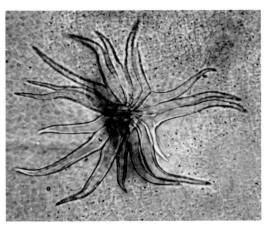

Branched hair on cleared and stained ivy leaf (Stomata in the epidermis are also apparent)

Top view of a branched hair on grape ivy cleared leaf

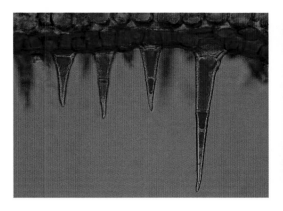

Hairs with **anthocyanin** pigments on the lower **epidermis** of an African violet leaf

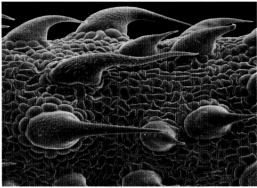

Hairs on hemp leaf (SEM)

Which plant hairs are being used as a model to design material to capture bedbugs?

Recently, a scientist in the USA has been developing a material to trap bedbugs based on the hooked **hairs** found on bean leaves. These hairs protect leaves from being eaten by various insects by puncturing their bodies as they crawl over the leaf surface.

'Hooked' hairs on bean leaf

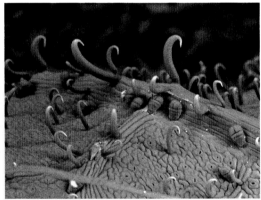

'Hooked' hairs on scarlet runner bean leaf (SEM)

What is the function of exceptionally long hairs such as those of Old Man Cactus?

These long, white hairs deflect sunlight which helps protect the stem from drying out.

What causes the pungent aroma when leaves of plants such as geraniums, tomatoes, sage, and mints are rubbed?

Hairs on these leaves contain aromatic compounds, many of which deter insects. These compounds occur either in a single spherical cell or a group of cells at the tip of the hair. Rubbing leaves damages these cells and releases their contents.

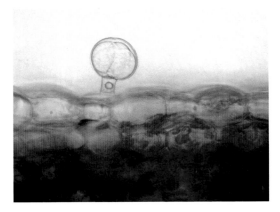

Secretory hair on garden sage leaf

Garden sage leaves

Secretory hair on tomato leaf

Secretory hairs on African violet leaf

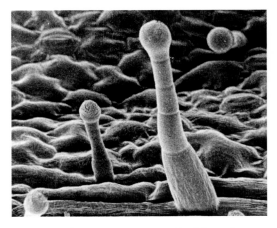

Secretory hairs on geranium leaf (SEM)

Secretion from geranium leaf hair (SEM)

What is the source of hallucinogens in marijuana plants?

Leaves and flowers of marijuana plants are covered with hairs, some of which secrete hallucinogenic compounds such as tetrahydrocannabinol (THC).

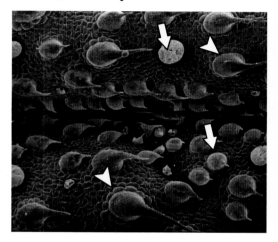

Secretory hairs (arrows) and non-secretory hairs (arrowheads) on marijuana leaf (SEM)

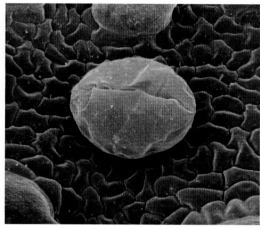

Higher magnification of secretory hairs on marijuana leaf (SEM)

Why are stinging nettles so painful when touched?

The leaves and stems of stinging nettles have numerous, unbranched, multicellular **hairs**. Each hair is hollow and consists of an upper needle-like portion and a bulbous base that contains **histamines** and other chemicals. The upper part breaks upon contact and the chemicals are released when the broken hair tip penetrates the skin. The chemicals cause a burning and itching sensation that can be quite painful.

Hairs on stem of stinging nettle

Hairs on stem and **petioles** of stinging nettle

Why are some species of *Dieffenbachia* called dumbcane?

All parts of these plants, including the leaves, contain large numbers of needle-shaped calcium oxalate crystals. If these are ingested they cause painful burning and swelling of the lips, tongue, and throat. Speaking may become difficult and this accounts for the name dumbcane. The prevalence of these calcium oxalate crystals protects leaves from being eaten by herbivores.

Leaves of dumbcane

Needle-like crystals viewed with polarized light

What chemical substance in poison ivy is responsible for its adverse effects on some people?

All parts of the plant, including leaves, produce an oily resin, **urushiol**, a skin irritant that causes a rash in about half the population. A smaller percentage of people are very sensitive and may develop painful blisters. Even smoke from burning plants can irritate skin, eyes, and lungs.

Poison ivy leaves

Poison ivy leaves in fall

How do Venus flytraps capture insects?

The large, central vein of the leaf acts as a hinge. On each leaf half there are three large "trigger" **hairs** that are sensitive to the touch. If one of these is stimulated three times, e.g. by an insect walking on the leaf, the leaf snaps shut, trapping the insect. Large hairs on the surface of the leaf then secrete enzymes that digest the insect and absorb the resulting products.

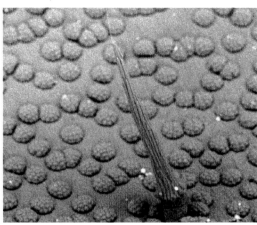

Leaves of Venus flytrap

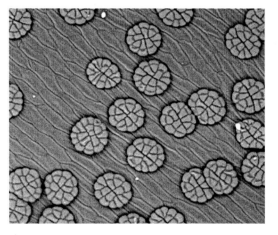

Top view of enzyme-secreting, multicellular hairs on surface of Venus fly trap leaf (SEM)

Top view of a long trigger hair on surface of Venus fly trap leaf (SEM)

What are the green bumps that often occur on wild grape leaves?

These bumps are galls caused by an aphid-like insect. The female feeds on the leaf and in so doing induces leaf cells to divide forming a **gall**. She lays eggs in the gall and these will hatch into nymphs that derive nutrients from the gall tissue.

What are pitcher plants?

Pitcher plants grow in nitrogen-poor, boggy conditions and augment their nitrogen supply by trapping and digesting insects and even small animals. The name "pitcher plant" is derived from its modified leaf that resembles a pitcher. The rim of the pitcher is often coloured to attract insects, and **nectar** may be secreted as a reward.

The lip of the pitcher is coated with a film of water, causing insects to slip and fall into the pitcher. Once there, a combination of loose **wax** flakes and large, downward pointing **hairs** on its epidermal surface prevent the insects from climbing out. Specialized hairs at the base of the pitcher secrete enzymes that digest the trapped prey, releasing nitrogen and other elements that are then absorbed by the plant.

Pitcher plants (**Sarracenia purpurea**) in an Ontario bog

Pitcher of a **Nepenthes** species

What are the black spots that develop on the leaves of many maple species?

These black spots are caused by a fungus that causes a disease called tar spot. The spots are the reproductive structures containing **spores** of the fungus. This disease is particularly prevalent during wet summers.

Tar spots on maple leaves

IV. FLOWERS

Photo by Hugh T. Lemon

IV. Flowers
Do all plants have flowers?

There are several groups of plants such as mosses, ferns, and conifers that lack flowers. These groups are all more primitive than the flowering plants. Since mosses and ferns do not have flowers they do not produce seeds. In ferns, **spores** are formed within structures called **sporangia**, usually appearing in groups as brown spots on the undersides of leaves. The patterns of these groups vary depending on the species of fern. When mature, the spores are released, fall to the ground and develop into small, free-living plants (**gametophytes**) that bear the male and female sex organs.

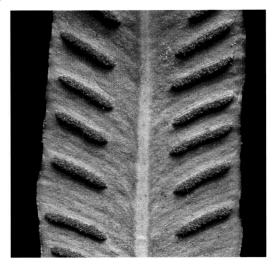

Groups of Sporangia of **Asplenium scolopendrium**

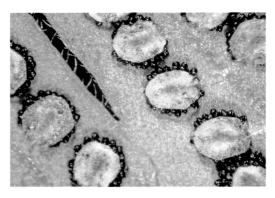

Covered sporangia of **Thelypteris dentata**

Sporangia on leaf of
Polypodium crassifolium

Sporangia (arrowheads) of Ostrich fern containing spores (arrows)

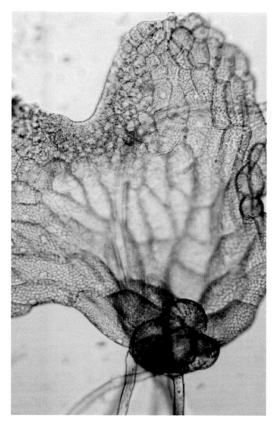

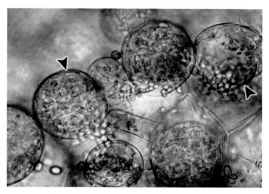

Fern male sex organs (arrowheads) containing sperm

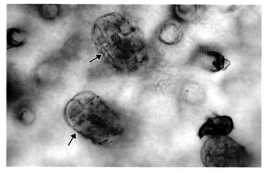

Fern gametophyte

Fern female sex organs (arrows) each containing a single egg cell. Sperm swim to the female structure in a film of water and fertilize the egg

Conifers, such as pines, spruces, and firs do not have flowers but they do form seeds. The reproductive structures of conifers are male and female cones. Male cones are small and short-lived. They produce copious amounts of **pollen** that is carried by wind to the larger female cones where **fertilization** and seed formation occurs.

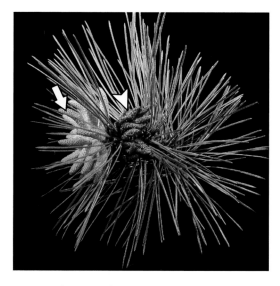

New male cones (arrow) and old male cones (arrowhead) of white pine

Male cones of a pine species

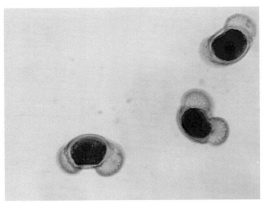

Winged pine pollen

Female cone of Douglas fir

Mature female cones of pine

Young female (red) and male (light brown)
cones of spruce

Fleshy female cone of yew

What types of plants that still exist today were prevalent during the time of the dinosaurs?

Plants related to present-day cycads, ground pines, horsetails, ferns (including seed ferns), and some conifers, especially the monkey puzzle trees, existed at the time of dinosaurs. None of these primitive plants had flowers.

Lycopodiella clavatum, a ground pine

Diphasiastrum digitatum, a ground pine

Branched horsetail species

Reproductive structures (strobili) of horsetail

Unbranched horsetail species

Dryopteris ferns

Ostrich ferns

Dicksonia fibrosa, a tree fern

Cyathea poeppigii, a tree fern
(Photo by Andrea Reid)

Monkey puzzle trees
(Photo by Maria Paula Toledo)

Monkey puzzle tree with cones
(Photo by Maria Paula Toledo)

Which plant group has flowers?

The largest and most diverse group of plants, the **angiosperms**, has flowers. Species with flowers evolved towards the end of the dinosaur era. Present-day flowers show tremendous variation in size, colour, and complexity. As flower types evolved, so did many of the insects and other animals that served as pollinators.

Scarlet bee balm flowers

Trailing *Lobelia* flowers

Marsh marigold flowers

Petunia flowers

What are the essential parts of flowers?

Flowers function in sexual reproduction. The essential structures for this event are the male and female parts. The male structures are the **stamens** with **anthers** that produce pollen. The female structures are the **carpels** (either individual or fused), each with an **ovary**, **style** and **stigma**. The ovary houses the **ovules**.

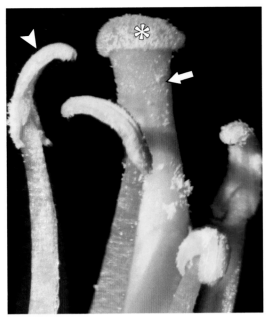

Stigma (✳), style (arrow) and anthers (arrowhead) of a canola flower

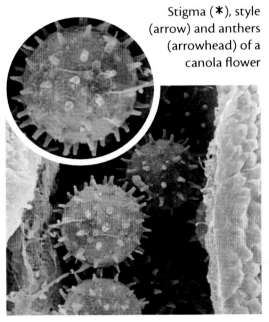

Pollen in **Hibiscus** anther (SEM)

Tulip flower with stamens (arrow), stigma (arrowhead) and ovary (✳)

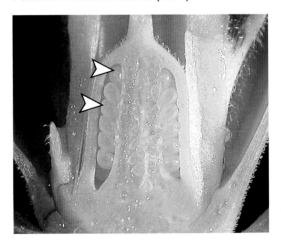

Ovules (arrowheads) in bisected **Hibiscus** ovary

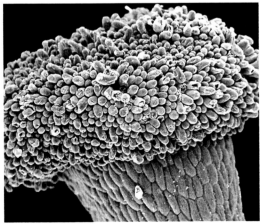

Stigma of **Hibiscus** flower (SEM)

Do grasses have flowers?

All grasses have flowers, but individually they are usually very small and not coloured since they do not depend on insects for **pollination**. The obvious reproductive structures of grasses are groups of flowers called **inflorescences**. In ornamental grasses these are large and showy. The **stamens** of the flowers elongate so that the **pollen** can be dispersed by wind.

Yellow stamens of brome grass flowers

Inflorescences of brome grass

Ornamental grasses with large inflorescences (arrows)

Do broad-leaved trees have flowers?

Broad-leaved trees are angiosperms and therefore all of them have flowers. In many tree species, flowers open and pollination occurs in the spring before leaves develop.

Magnolia in bloom

Norway maple flowers

American basswood flowers

Horse chestnut flowers

Tulip tree flower

What are the tassels on corn plants?

Corn is an example of a wind-pollinated plant with separate male and female flowers on the same plant. Tassels, located above the female flowers, are groups of male flowers. **Pollen**, produced in their **stamens**, is carried by the wind to female flowers.

Tassels on field corn plants

Tassels with stamens (arrows) on field corn

What are the 'silks' on ears of corn?

In corn, groups of female flowers are encased in leafy husks along the plant stem. Each female flower consists of an ovary and an elongated style commonly called a 'silk'. Each style has a terminal stigma that catches the wind-borne pollen. A pollen grain germinates on the tip of the stigma and a **pollen tube** grows down the greatly elongated style, carrying the sperm nucleus to an ovule for fertilization and seed formation.

Young corn cob in field

Corn silks and young **kernels**

Mature corn cob with many individual fruits

What are 'pussy willows'?

The showy 'pussy willows' are male inflorescences known as catkins.

Pussy willows in spring

Male catkins

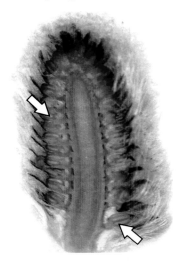

Cut male pussy willow catkin with young stamens (arrows)

Mature stamens that have elongated in male catkins

What types of flowers are pollinated by wind?

The flowers of such plants usually have dull colours, small or no petals, and do not produce **nectar**. In many cases, the **stamens** elongate so that the **pollen** produced can be dispersed by the wind. In wind-pollinated trees, the male flowers mature before leaf development to enhance pollen dispersal.

Silver maple flower with extended stamens

Why do so many plants have flowers with coloured petals?

Plants have co-evolved with various pollinators such as bees, butterflies, moths, birds, and small mammals. Petals (or other plant parts) have specific colours that are cues to a source of nutrients such as **nectar** and **pollen** for pollinators. As the animals feed and move from plant to plant they carry pollen.

Red *Hibiscus* flowers are pollinated by hummingbirds

Sedum flowers are pollinated by bees

Brightly coloured daylilies are pollinated by bees

Many native flowering plant species depend on bees for **pollination**. A healthy population of these insects is also critical for the production of fruit and canola crops.

Sturt's desert pea flowers are pollinated by birds

Crab apple flowers are pollinated by bees

Pear flowers are pollinated by bees

What is responsible for the various colours of flowers?

Most flowers that are red, purple or blue have a water-soluble pigment called **anthocyanin** that is contained in **vacuoles** in their cells.

Grape hyacinth

Double tulip

Coneflower **inflorescence**

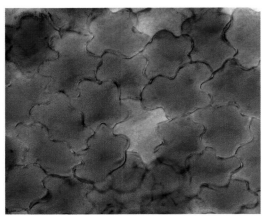

Anthocyanins in petal cells of an African violet variety

Flowers that are yellow or orange have pigments called **carotenoids**. These consist of **carotenes** and **xanthophylls** that are located in **plastids** (**chromoplasts**) within some of their cells.

Daffodil flowers

Hawkweed inflorescence

Yellow pansy flowers

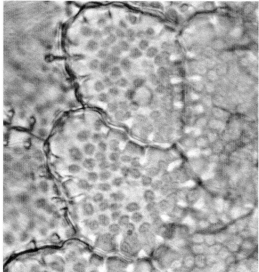

Yellow **chromoplasts** in petal cells of pansy

Bird of paradise flower

Chromoplasts in cells of an orange
petal of bird of paradise flower

How are the colours of flowers perceived by bees?

Bees do not see flower colours in the same way as humans. Unlike humans, their eyes are constructed to be sensitive to wavelengths in the ultraviolet range.

Aster inflorescences as viewed by humans
(Photo by Peter Kevan)

Aster inflorescences as viewed by a bee
(Photo by Peter Kevan)

Wild blue flax flower seen by humans
(Photo by Peter Kevan)

Wild blue flax flower seen by bees
(Photo by Peter Kevan)

How are some plants with white or lightly coloured flowers pollinated?

Magnolia flowers have many **stamens** that produce large amounts of pollen. Beetles use pollen as a food source and, while feeding, act as pollinators.

Magnolia acuminata

Magnolia stellata
(Photo by Christopher Peterson)

Moth-pollinated flowers tend to be white and tubular in shape. They open at night, produce large amounts of nectar, and have strong scents. Examples are yucca and some tobacco species.

Moth-pollinated
tobacco flowers

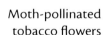

Yucca flowers

Open yucca flower

Why do some bees find certain orchid flowers strangely attractive?

Flowers of some orchids are highly specialized so as to mimic female bees. These "bee orchid" flowers attract males that attempt to mate with the flower, thus picking up **pollen** and later transferring it to another flower.

Flowers of a bee orchid
(Photo by Günter Gerlach)

What is unusual about the surface of flower petals?

The epidermal cells of petals are tightly packed together and most do not have **stomata**. Petals are covered with a **cuticle** that is often unevenly thickened and ridged. Cells of red geranium petals have wall ingrowths that add an unusual pattern to the **epidermis**. These help to strengthen the petals.

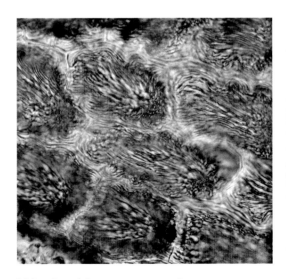

Ridged cuticle on pansy petal

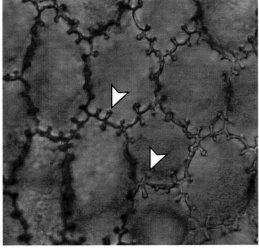

Geranium petal epidermal cells with wall ingrowths (arrowheads)

Why do the epidermal cells of many petals have a conical shape?

It has recently been discovered that these projecting cells allow large bees, such as bumblebees, to grab hold of the petal with their claws while foraging for **nectar** or **pollen**.

Lantana flowers

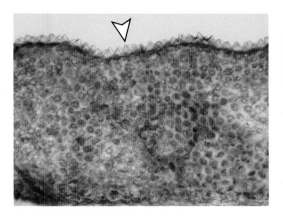

Section of **Lantana** petal with conical epidermal cells (arrowhead)

Conical epidermal cells in a top view of **Lantana** petal

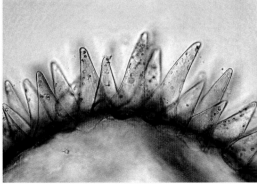

Conical-shaped epidermal cells on pansy petal

Variation in colour of pansies

Why do flowers have nectar and where is it produced?

Nectar is a food reward for pollinators such as bees, butterflies, moths, and birds. Many flowers have specialized structures called **nectaries**. These produce the sugar-rich **nectar**. Nectaries are extremely variable in structure and location.

Canola flowers

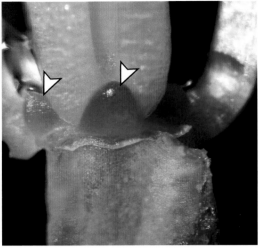

Nectaries (arrowheads) in a canola flower

When is a 'flower' not a flower?

What we commonly call flowers in plants such as sunflowers, coneflowers, and daisies are actually **inflorescences** consisting of many closely packed, individual, small flowers. Those in the center are called "disk flowers" and have both **carpels** and **stamens**, but very reduced petals. Those around the edge are called "ray flowers". These tend to be sterile and have one large, showy petal. Together the disk and ray flowers act as a single large flower that attracts pollinators.

Inflorescence of coneflower

Inflorescences of Shasta daisy

Sunflower inflorescence with ray and disk flowers

Cut-away view showing many disk flowers (arrowhead) and a few ray flowers (arrow) **Inset** - Disk flower with fused petals (arrow) and protruding dark stigmas

The large showy structures in poinsettias are modified leaves that attract hummingbirds as pollinators. The actual flowers are the central, small, green and red parts. The yellow structures are nectaries. These produce large amounts of nectar that is food for hummingbirds as well as some insects.

Red modified leaves in poinsettia

Reduced flower (arrow) and yellow nectary (arrowhead) in poinsettia

In the flamingo plant, the large colourful structure is a modified leaf called a **spathe.** The actual flowers are yellow, very small, and are located on the projecting **spadix.** Horticulturists breed this species to produce variously coloured spathes.

Red spathe and small yellow flowers of a flamingo plant

How do sunflowers turn towards the sun?

Blue light (part of the visible spectrum) triggers a response referred to as solar tracking. In sunflowers, it is the **inflorescence** that tilts towards the sun. This movement is caused by changes in special cells below the inflorescence. These cells enlarge or shrink according to the pressure of their contents against the cell walls. The pressure increases in the cells on one side causing cells to expand. At the same time the pressure decreases in cells on the opposite side, causing the cells to shrink. The difference in pressure forces the inflorescence to tilt.

A field of sunflowers turned towards the sun

What is the tallest flower in the world?

The Titan arum, native to Sumatra, produces a flower (actually an **inflorescence**) that can reach up to 3 meters (10 feet) in height. These plants rarely flower, and when they do the flower lasts only one or two days. During this time it emits a foul odour resembling rotten meat that attracts flies and carrion-beetles as pollinators.

Titan arum in the Bovey Greenhouse, University of Guelph (Photo by Roger Tschanz)

What are the smallest flowering plants?

These are the duckweeds. They are floating plants that range in size from one to three millimeters. Each plant has one to three leaves; some species lack roots while others have very small roots. All species have small flowers, and in the genus **Wolffia** they are only 0.3 millimeters in length. The flowers consist of only two **stamens** and a single **carpel**. Duckweeds can spread rapidly by the formation of buds at the bases of their leaves.

Floating duckweed plants

Which plant group has members that flower only in intervals of 65 – 120 years?

Species of bamboo flower after very long periods of growth. All plants in a bamboo forest will flower at the same time and then the above-ground parts die back. Since they have underground **rhizome** systems, new shoots are regenerated and the plants go through the cycle again.

Bamboo species in Thailand
(Photo by Christopher Peterson)

Bamboo forest near Kyoto, Japan

Which plant family has the most complex flowers?

The orchid family (Orchidaceae) has the most highly evolved flowers of all plants. Although highly varied, they have one thing in common - they are not radially symmetrical and often have unusual shapes. The Orchidaceae is the largest family of flowering plants: the numerous species (about 24,000) inhabit many climatic zones from the tropics to the northern tundra. Although many orchids are rooted in the ground others, especially in the tropics, are **epiphytes**, i.e. they perch on other plants.

Yellow lady slipper orchid

Eastern prairie fringed orchid
(Photo by Hugh T. Lemon)

Showy lady's slipper orchid
(Photo by Hugh T. Lemon)

Fairy slipper orchid

Flowers of an ornamental *Phalaenopsis*

Why is Jimsonweed sometimes called the 'Devil's trumpet'?

Jimsonweed or **Datura** plants have large, attractive, trumpet-shaped flowers that make the species a favorite among gardeners. However, their leaves, flowers and seeds have compounds that may cause hallucinations and delirium. If consumed in large enough quantities, seeds and tea made from the seeds can be fatal. The blood thinner, warfarin, was first discovered in this species.

Jimsonweed flower

Jimsonweed fruits and seeds

Why are dandelions so abundant?

Dandelions have two means of propagation. A dandelion 'flower' is actually an **inflorescence** of many flowers. Each flower produces a one-seeded fruit with a plume-like portion that enables wind dispersal over wide areas. In addition, dandelions are rather unusual in that **pollination** is not required for the development of seeds.

Dandelion inflorescences and plumed fruits

A second means of dandelion propagation involves the formation of new shoots on roots. Even small pieces of roots left in the soil can produce new plants, making these plants difficult to eradicate once they are established.

Dandelion shoots growing from roots

Why do some pollen grains elicit an allergic reaction?

Pollen grains are covered with proteins that are species-specific and are important for **pollination**. It is these **proteins** that cause an allergic reaction in many people.

Leaves of ragweed plants

Inflorescences of ragweed plants with mostly male flowers (arrow)

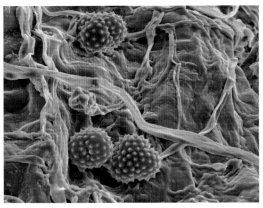

Ragweed pollen grains (SEM)
(Photo by Sandy Smith)

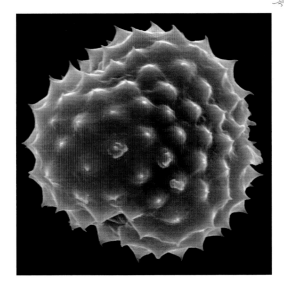

Ragweed pollen grain (SEM)
(Photo by Sandy Smith)

How is pollen used in the petroleum industry and in monitoring climate change?

The outer walls of some **pollen** grains are preserved as fossils dating back millions of years. It is possible to identify plant species from the features of these walls. When assessing a region for potential oil deposits, deep soil cores are taken and features of the pollen recovered are used to identify plant species that may be associated with oil deposits. This information is used by oil companies in determining sites for drilling.

The same features of pollen can be used by climatologists to determine past climatic conditions because many plant species are associated with certain climates.

What are capers?

Capers are flower buds from a Mediterranean plant, known as caper bush or Flinders rose. The buds are sundried and then pickled in vinegar or wine. They are used to add a unique flavour to food.

Closed flower buds (capers)

Why do cut flowers often wilt after being transferred to water in a vase?

Cutting a stem breaks the continuity of the water columns in water-conducting cells and air is sucked into the stem. This air creates bubbles in some of the water-conducting cells, preventing them from transporting water from the vase to the flowers. Cutting the stem also allows bacteria and fungi to enter these cells. They can be clogged up with the micro-organisms or their gummy secretions. Because of these events, cut flowers wilt sooner than those remaining on the plant.

Wilting cut lilies

What is the most primitive flowering plant that still exists today?

Amborella trichopoda, a small shrub found only on the island of New Caledonia, is the most primitive living flowering plant. The small male and female flowers are found on separate plants. Both flower types lack showy petals.

Male flowers of *Amborella trichopoda* (Photo by Usher Posluszny)

Female flower of *Amborella trichopoda* (Photo by Usher Posluszny)

What induces plants to flower?

Some species such as bean, corn, cotton, cucumber and tomato can bloom any time during the year. In these cases, the controlling factor is a specific number of leaves that must be produced before flowers can form. These species are called day-neutral plants. Most species, however, respond to night-length. Species that bloom in the spring or fall must experience dark periods longer than a critical amount. These species are called short-day plants. Examples are poinsettias, asters, chrysanthemums, and strawberries. On the other hand, plants that normally bloom in the summer respond to dark periods shorter than a critical length. These are long-day species and include spinach, lettuce, potatoes, petunias, and **Rudbeckia**. The processes involved in these plant responses to dark periods are complex and involve a special pigment called **phytochrome**.

Tomato, a day-neutral plant

Bean, a day-neutral plant

Chrysanthemum variety, a short-day plant

Asters are short-day plants

Rudbeckia, a long-day plant

Lettuce, a long-day plant

84

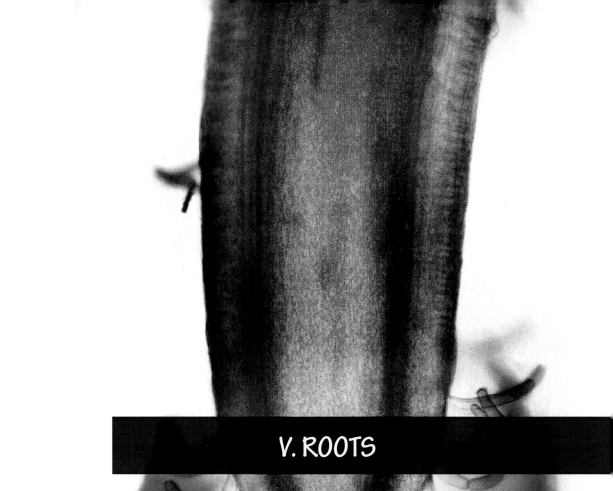
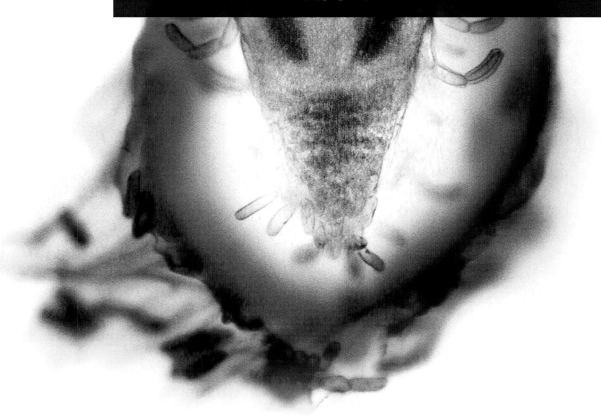

V. ROOTS

V. Roots

How do root systems develop to anchor the shoot?

The first structure to emerge from a germinating seed is the root. It immediately grows into the soil, anchoring the seedling. After the first root reaches a certain length, branch roots are initiated near the central vascular system of the main root. These grow outward and eventually emerge at right angles to the main root. Branch roots help to stabilize the growing shoot. In many plants, the initial branch roots will, subsequently, branch to form an extensive root system.

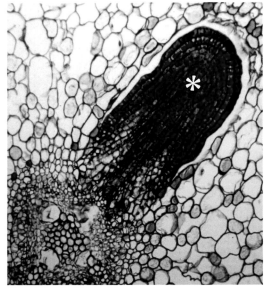

Stained willow root cross section with young branch root (✱) that has not yet emerged from the main root

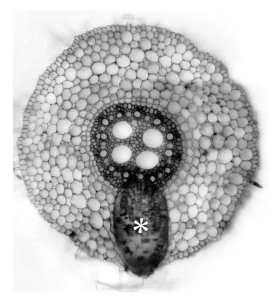

Stained corn root cross section with a young branch root (✱)

Extensively branched root system of a small spruce tree

How do roots grow through soil without injuring themselves?

The only part of the root that grows is the tip. The delicate dividing cells in the **apical meristem** are covered by a protective **root cap**. Peripheral root cap cells are shed and are constantly replaced by cells generated by the root apical meristem as the root grows into the soil. Root cap cells exude slippery substances that help the root grow between soil particles without damaging the tip.

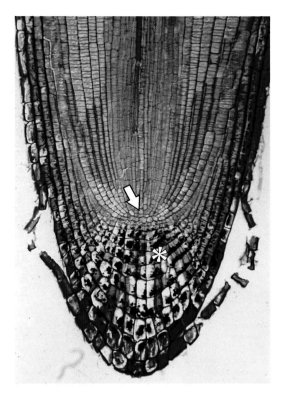

Stained longitudinal section of a white mustard root apex with the root cap (✱) covering the apical meristem (arrow)

Root tip of corn with purple-stained slippery substances

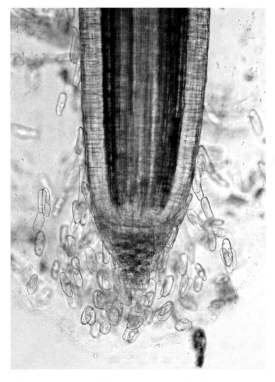

Grass root tip with numerous shed root cap cells

How does root structure aid in absorption of water and mineral ions from the soil?

The extensive branching of root systems increases their surface areas and aids in accessing water and ions. The outermost layer of roots consists of epidermal cells that are tightly packed together. These cells are not covered with a **cuticle** so that water and ions can enter the root. In addition, some epidermal cells form unbranched **root hairs**. These provide increased surface areas for taking up water and nutrient ions.

Roots on a corn seedling

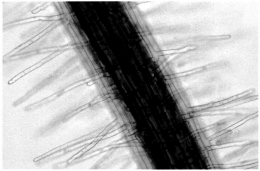

Hairs protruding from a grass seedling root

Why are the roots of 90% of all plant species associated with fungi?

Many soils become depleted of mineral nutrients, especially adjacent to roots. Plants have evolved with various groups of beneficial fungi to form symbiotic associations known as **mycorrhizas** (literally 'fungus roots'). The thread-like strands (**mycelium**) of the fungus spread out from roots into the soil for long distances. These tap into water and essential mineral elements such as phosphorus and nitrogen, and transport them back to the plant. In turn, since fungi cannot photosynthesize, they depend on the plant for sugars and other organic compounds. Tree species such as pine, fir, spruce and birch are associated with fungi that form reproductive structures commonly called mushrooms or toadstools. These are often located around the bases of trees. The fungal mycelium closely associated with tree roots forms a covering that may have a distinctive colour.

Mycorrhizal mushrooms associated with white pine seedling (Photo by Christian Godbout)

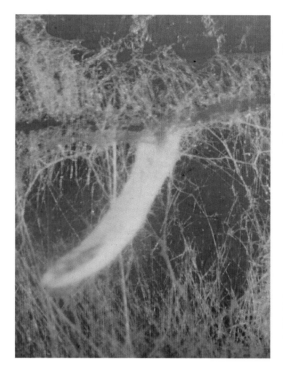

Douglas fir mycorrhizal roots
(Photo by Hugues Massicotte)

White fungal mycelium associated with alder roots

American beech mycorrhizal roots (natural colour)

Most plants, including nearly all crop and horticultural species, are associated with mycorrhizal fungi that remain below the soil surface. These fungi reproduce by means of small single-celled structures called **spores** that are produced by **mycelium** in the soil. These spores can be recovered and used to identify fungal species. When roots are colonized, the fungus can only be seen by clearing the roots and examining them with a microscope. Highly branched fungal structures are formed within living root cells to increase the surface area for exchange of subtances between the symbiotic partners.

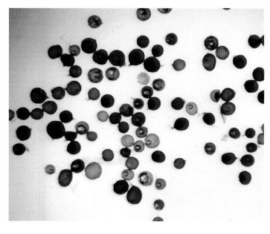

Multicoloured spores of various mycorrhizal fungi. The spores were extracted from soil adjacent to purple loosestrife plants

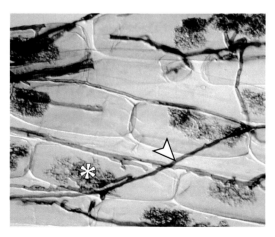

Branched fungal structures (✻) and hyphae (arrowhead) within cleared and stained leek root (Photo by Mark Brundrett)

How is it possible for most non-green plants to survive?

Plants such as Indian pipe, the snow plant, and some orchid species lack **chlorophyll** and are unable to produce their own food. Therefore, they depend on fungi to survive. In these cases, the **mycelium** of a fungus links the roots of these plants to the roots of green plants. The fungus transports sugars from the green plant to the non-photosynthetic plant. Since the fungus does not gain anything from the association with the non-photosynthetic plant, the latter are often called 'cheaters'.

Indian pipe plants

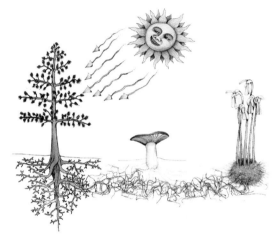

Diagram showing fungal **hyphae** connecting a photosynthetic tree to Indian pipe plants (Drawing by Lewis Melville)

Flowering shoot of the snow plant (Photo by Hugues Massicotte)

Flowers of the Australian orchid, **Rhizanthella gardneri** (Photo by Mark Brundrett)

Why does planting legumes (e.g. soybeans, beans, peas, alfalfa) increase the supply of nitrogen in the soil?

Nodules (arrowheads) on pea roots

Nitrogen is one of the essential elements frequently depleted in agricultural soils. Legumes, in combination with certain bacteria (mostly **Rhizobium** species), develop **root nodules** within which the bacteria are housed. The interior of the nodule is an oxygen-poor environment that allows the bacteria to capture atmospheric nitrogen. Some of this nitrogen can then be used by the plant to synthesize compounds such as amino acids and proteins. These compounds become available for growth processes in the plant. During harvesting, the legume roots remain in the soil where they decompose, releasing their nitrogenous chemicals.

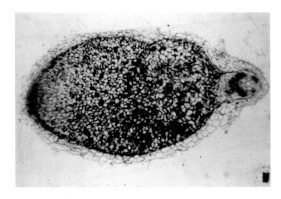

Section of pea root nodule filled with bacteria

How do epiphytic orchids obtain mineral ions and water?

Many tropical orchids are **epiphytes** (i.e., they grow on other plants but are not parasites). Such orchids are typically found perched on tree branches to attain a position high in the canopy with improved access to light. However, the roots of such plants are not in soil. Epiphytic orchids have adapted to this mode of existence by producing two types of roots. The first type grows into organic matter collected in the crotches of tree branches; these roots absorb both water and ions. The second type of root grows into the air at odd angles from the plant and is an example of an **aerial root**. These roots have a multilayered **epidermis**, the **velamen**. Its cells are dead but they have strong, lignified strips in their walls that prevent collapse. When these cells are full of air they reflect light, giving the roots a whitish aspect. During a rainfall, the velamen soaks up water and retains it like a sponge. This water can be used by the plant during dry periods. Cells adjacent to the velamen have many **chloroplasts** and, through **photosynthesis**, can contribute to the food supply of the plant. Several species lack leaves and rely totally on aerial roots for their food!

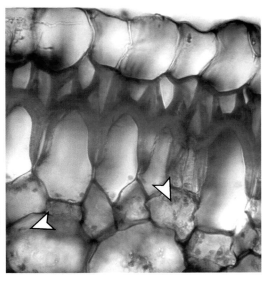

Aerial roots (arrows) of an epiphytic orchid **Inset** - Sections of an aerial root showing green interior

Chloroplasts (arrowheads) in stained section of aerial root of an orchid

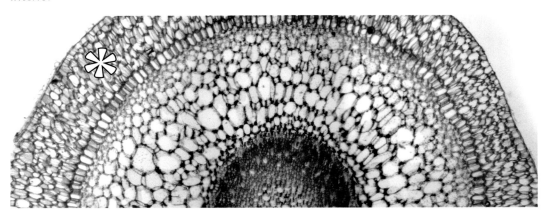

Stained section of an aerial orchid root showing a multilayered velamen (✱)

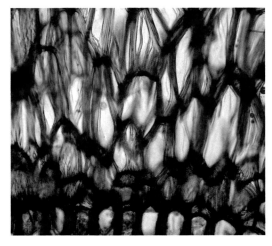

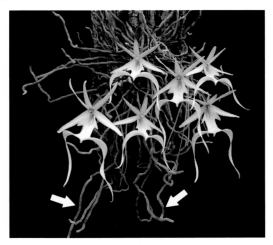

Strips of **lignin** (stained blue) in velamen cells

Aerial roots (arrows) and flowers of the leafless Ghost orchid (Photo by Keith Davis)

What are the 'knees' found around the base of bald cypress trees?

These knobby structures are highly modified, thickened roots that grow upward and emerge from the soil. They have numerous air spaces that are continuous with the air spaces in the underground roots. The above-ground parts of the roots are important in providing oxygen to the roots that are often submerged in water or grow in very wet soil.

'Knees' (arrows) around base of bald cypress tree growing in very wet soil

Bald cypress tree

How are mangroves able to grow in brackish water?

These plants have to cope with lack of oxygen in the root environment as well as excessive salt. A supply of oxygen for the submerged roots is obtained from roots that grow upward into the atmosphere. Much of the salt is screened out by specialized cell layers in roots. In addition, salt glands present on leaves secrete excess salt to avoid cell damage.

Mangroves in brackish water showing roots emerging into the atmosphere

Why do large split-leaf philodendrons develop aerial roots?

In the tropics, these plants twine around tree trunks in order to access sunlight for photosynthesis. To augment the original root system for nutrient and water absorption, new roots are formed along the stem. These elongate and eventually grow into the ground.

Aerial roots (arrows) developing from the stem of a split-leaf philodendron

Aerial roots (arrowheads) growing into the soil

94

VI. SOME COMMERCIAL PRODUCTS FROM PLANTS

VI. Some commercial products from plants

What is the source of natural rubber?

The rubber tree produces **latex** (that includes rubber particles) in specialized structures called **laticifers**. These tubular structures are located near the periphery of the tree trunk. The latex, obtained by making diagonal slashes into the trunk, is collected and processed into rubber.

Tapping a rubber tree for latex in Vietnam (Photo by John Lott)

What plant part is used to make the textile called cotton?

Cotton is made from long **hairs** that have grown from the epidermis of cotton seeds. The seeds develop within a fruit (commonly referred to as a boll). When the fruit ripens and splits open, the seeds with their long hairs are exposed. The hairs would normally aid in wind dispersal of the seeds. However, these hairs, consisting largely of **cellulose**, can be separated from the seeds mechanically and woven into cotton cloth.

Cotton fruit beginning to open

Cotton bolls

What plant part is used to make linen?

Linen is manufactured from unusual fibers in the stems of flax plants. These fibers are very long (reaching up to 56 centimeters) and have very thick walls that consist mainly of **cellulose**.

The individual fibers are grouped into bundles that can be extracted from the stem by a process called '**retting**'. In this ancient technique, bacteria decompose the soft parts of the stem but leave the fiber bundles intact. The absence of lignin in the fiber walls accounts for the flexible nature of linen cloth.

Flax flowers (Photo by Jean Gerrath)

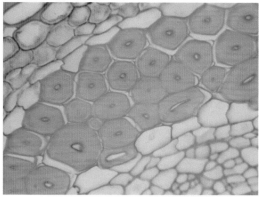

Thick-walled fibers in cross section of a flax stem

Are there natural sources of fibers other than cotton and flax for clothing?

One plant species that has a long history of being grown for its fibers is hemp. Individual fibers in this plant can be as long as 2 meters (6 feet)! The original textile (denim) used by Levi Strauss for making jeans came from hemp. Today, hemp is seeing a renewed importance as a textile for clothing and other items. It is also used to make rope and canvas.

Fields of hemp grown for fibers
(Photos by Julie Simpson)

What is the most expensive spice?

The colourful flavouring spice, saffron, is the most expensive of all herbs and spices. This is because it consists of the red **stigmas** of saffron crocus flowers. These stigmas are picked by hand. It takes over 150 flowers to make one gram of the spice!

Crocus flowers with orange/red stigmas

What is the source of pectin that is used to thicken jams and jellies?

Pectins are extracted from plant tissues containing cells with high amounts of **pectic substances** in their walls. The main sources of commercial pectin are dried citrus peels and apples. In the plant, these gummy substances serve to "glue" the cells together.

Lemon, lime, and orange peels

Apple fruit pieces

What is the source of chocolate?

All chocolate comes from the seeds of one tree species, the cocoa tree. An unusual feature of this plant is that the flowers develop on the trunk of the tree and, therefore, the fruits containing the seeds occur on the trunk.

Split cacao fruit with seeds

Fruits on a cacao tree trunk

What is the source of vanilla?

Vanilla is named for the vanilla orchid plant native to Mexico. Vanilla is extracted from its pods (also called beans) and seeds.

Vanilla flower (Photo by Noris Ledesma)

Vanilla pods (Photo by Noris Ledesma)

Which plant has seeds that are important sources of oil but are also poisonous?

Castor bean (*Ricinus communis*) has seeds that contain large quantities of oils that are extracted and sold as castor oil. Castor oil was formerly used as a laxative but now it plays an important role as a component of soaps and lubricants. However, the seeds also contain ricin, a highly toxic **protein**. This toxin is inactivated with heat during oil extraction. Ricin can be obtained from non-heated seeds, and small quantities can be fatal to humans. Several high profile cases of intentional ricin poisoning have been reported.

Castor bean plant

Castor bean seeds

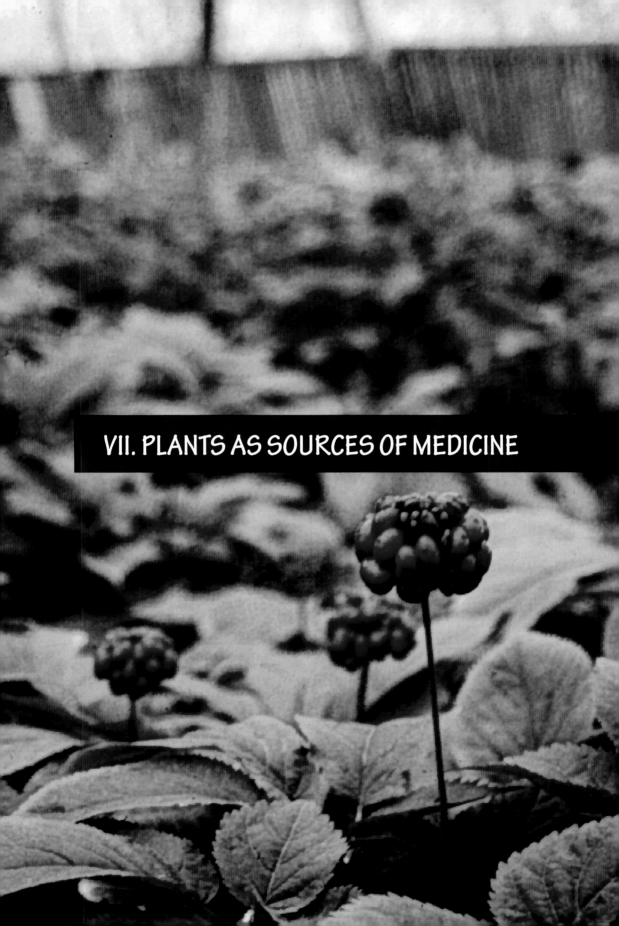

VII. PLANTS AS SOURCES OF MEDICINE

VII. Plants as sources of medicine

Which plant species have been used as sources of cancer drugs?

Pacific yew and other yew species produce the **alkaloid** taxol, an effective drug against some ovarian and breast cancers. The bark is particularly rich in this chemical.

Madagascar periwinkle produces two alkaloids, vinblastine and vincristine, that are used in the treatment of types of leukemia and lymphoma. The alkaloids of Pacific yew and periwinkle are now being synthesized in laboratories.

Leaves of a yew species

Bark of Pacific yew (Photo by Daniel Mosquin)

Periwinkle

What is the most widely used natural medicine in the world?

Compounds derived from ginseng roots are thought to promote human health in a number of ways. For example, they are used to lower blood pressure and cholesterol levels. Tea made from ginseng roots is often used to reduce stress.

Ginseng roots

Ginseng plants

Which plant species has been used for centuries in the treatment of certain heart disorders?

Extracts of foxglove have been used for centuries to slow and increase the strength of heartbeats. Two substances, digoxin and digitoxin, found primarily in the leaves, are the most effective substances produced.

Foxglove leaves and flowers

Foxglove flowers

What is the active ingredient in aspirin?

Teas made from the bark of willow (**Salix**) were used for centuries to treat pain and other maladies. The effective component of the tea was determined to be **salicylic acid**, now produced synthetically in the form of aspirin.

Willow stems and leaves

Willow bark

Which poisonous plant has medicinal properties, and has also been used in the past by women to enhance their beauty?

Deadly nightshade or belladonna (beautiful woman) contains compounds, including **atropine**, that are useful as a heart stimulant following cardiac arrest, and for treating Parkinson's disease. One attribute of atropine is that it dilates pupils when applied to eyes. In the past, women in the Mediterranean region applied 'juices' from the plant to their eyes to make themselves more alluring.

Belladonna leaves and flower

Belladonna leaves and fruits

Which plant is an important source of medicinal compounds, some of which are illegally trafficked?

Opium poppy (*Papaver somniferum*) plants produce latex that contains many compounds including opium, morphine, and codeine. Morphine can be processed into heroin for the lucrative drug trade. Fields of opium poppies are grown, both legally and illegally, in many countries. Although latex is found throughout the plant, it is usually obtained from slits made in mature seed pods (capsules).

Opium poppy flowers

Latex exuding from slits made in a seed pod (Photo by Peter Facchini)

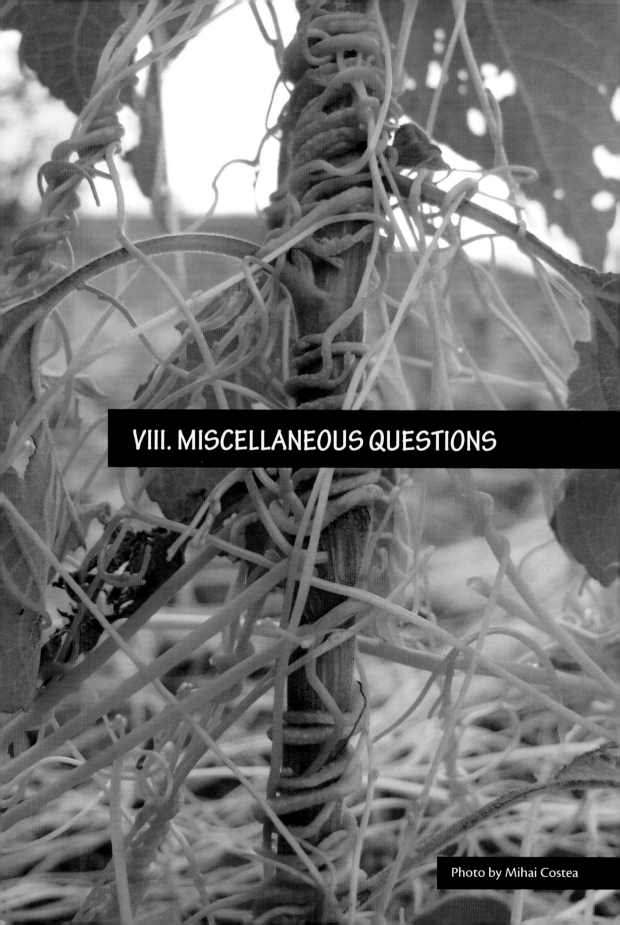

VIII. MISCELLANEOUS QUESTIONS

Photo by Mihai Costea

VIII. Miscellaneous questions

Which plants have the smallest seeds?

Flowers of **Spiranthes sinensis**
(Photo by Yukari Kuga)

Orchids are among a small group of plants that have what are commonly called 'dust seeds' because they are so tiny. The length of most orchid seeds is less than one millimeter. They are so light that they are dispersed by wind. Orchid seeds consist only of an undeveloped embryo. Since they lack stored food, they must become associated with symbiotic fungi in the soil in order for seed germination and seedling development to occur. These fungi break down plant litter and provide sugars for the developing embryo. However, seeds of commercially produced orchids can be germinated on a culture medium containing sugars; in this case there is no need for symbiotic fungi.

Seeds of the orchid **Spiranthes sinensis** being dispersed by wind (Photo by Yukari Kuga)

'Dust seeds' of **Spiranthes sinensis** next to a sewing needle (Photo by Yukari Kuga)

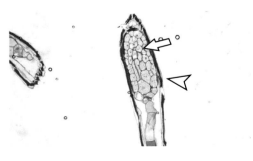

Section of a **Cattleya** orchid seed showing an undeveloped embryo (arrow) surrounded by a seed coat (arrowhead)

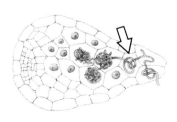

Drawing of an orchid embryo being invaded by a symbiotic fungus (arrow)

What are annual plants?

An annual plant is one that establishes itself from a seed. It grows and develops flowers and seeds within one year or less and then dies. Many important crops, including cereals and potatoes as well as ornamental plants are annuals.

Annual marigolds

Annual begonias

What are biennial plants?

A biennial plant is one that develops only shoots and roots in the first year, and then produces shoots, roots, flowers and seeds in the second year. During the first year, biennials store food in underground structures and this is used to promote early growth in the second year. Examples are carrots, sugar beets, parsley, burdock and sweet William.

Curley-leaf parsley in first year

Sweet William variety in second year

Burdock in first year

Burdock with flowers in second year

What are perennial plants?

A perennial plant is one that lives for more than two years. In non-woody perennial species, the above-ground plant parts usually die back each year but underground structures such as roots and rhizomes store nutrients and persist. New shoots form in the following year from these underground structures. In woody shrubs and trees, both above-ground (stems) and below-ground structures persist, but often leaves are shed.

Coltsfoot in early spring with old leaves from the previous season and new flowers

Lupins are a favorite garden perennial

Staghorn sumac, a perennial shrub

Alfalfa, a perennial forage crop

What causes galls on plant stems?

Several insect species induce changes in the growth of plant tissues resulting in structures called **galls**. Galls occur in many forms and may occur on stems, leaves, flowers, and roots. Once the gall forms, the insect lays eggs within it. Later, the hatched larvae gain nutrients for their growth before exiting the structure as an adult. The stem gall fly, for example, is responsible for gall formation in many goldenrod species.

Young gall on goldenrod stem

Mature galls on goldenrod stems

Exit hole in goldenrod gall

Galls caused by a gall wasp in some field rose species are quite spectacular in their structure. Each gall has several chambers, each containing a larva of the wasp.

Young stem galls (arrows) on wild rose species

Stem galls on wild rose

Larval chambers (arrows) in mature gall on wild rose stem

Larvae (arrows) in chambers of rose gall

In some willows, the willow pine cone gall midge stimulates shoot **apical meristems** to form many small scale leaves that resemble pine cones.

Pine cone-shaped galls on pussy willow stems in spring and winter

What is the 'milk' in milkweed plants?

When stems and leaves of milkweed plants are cut, a white substance is exuded. This is **latex**, a fluid that contains a number of toxic compounds, as well as rubber particles. Latex is produced in specialized long cells called **laticifers**. The toxic substances in latex defend the plant from chewing insects.

Milkweed flowers

Latex exuding from cut stem of milkweed

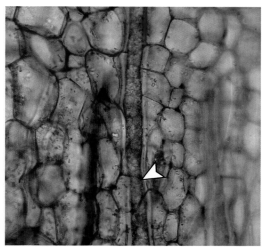

A stained longitudinal section of a stem with a laticifer (arrowhead)

Which plant species inspired the development of Velcro™?

Cocklebur has fruits that are covered with curved prickles that attach to the fur of animals to disperse seeds. George de Mestral, a Swiss citizen, noted this characteristic as he was removing such burs from his clothing. This gave him the idea for Velcro.

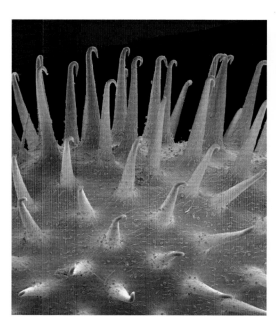

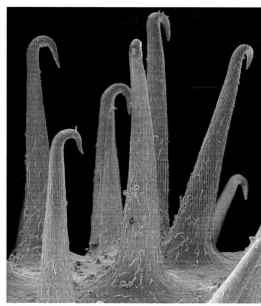

Hooked prickles on cocklebur fruits (SEM) (Photos by Sandy Smith)

Are some plants parasites?

There are several plant species that parasitize other plants. For example, dodders are often parasites on crop plants, and mistletoes are parasites on many tree species. Parasites attach themselves to host plants by specialized structures called **haustoria** that penetrate into stems. These structures absorb sugars and other nutrients and pass them to the parasite. Dodders and mistletoes can cause severe damage to their host plants, some of which are crop species.

Stems of dodder on a host plant
(Photo by Mihai Costea)

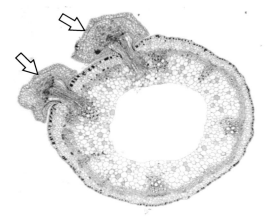

Stained cross section of a plant stem with haustoria (arrows) of dodder

European mistletoe on tree in Kyoto, Japan

Dwarf mistletoe on Lodgepole pine
(Photo by Kathryn Pernitsky)

Do plants get viruses?

Many plants are susceptible to viruses, and approximately two thousand different virus-caused plant diseases exist! In some cases one virus can infect several species of plants. For example, the tobacco mosaic virus not only infects tobacco plants but also crops such as tomatoes and peppers. Viral diseases cause billions of dollars in crop and horticultural losses worldwide each year. The colour pattern of some streaked tulip flowers is due to a viral infection that can be passed to future generations through the bulbs. Once a plant is infected by a virus, it has no way of recovering.

Virus-infected melon plants in a California field (Photo by William Wintermantel, USDA-ARS)

Close-up of virus-infected melon plants (Photo by William Wintermantel, USDA-ARS)

What is honeydew?

When an aphid feeds on a plant, it inserts its mouth part (stylet) into a sugar-conducting cell. The pressure in this cell, and cells to which it is connected, forces their contents into the aphid's digestive system. Since the aphid only uses a small amount of the sugar, most of the contents are excreted through its posterior!

The excreted droplet (**honeydew**) is sugar-rich and sticky. Honeydew is obvious on vehicles that are parked under trees infested with aphids. Crop plants can be severely damaged or even killed from the loss of sugars when they are heavily infested with these insects.

Aphid feeding and releasing 'honeydew' (Photo courtesy of Worth Publishers)

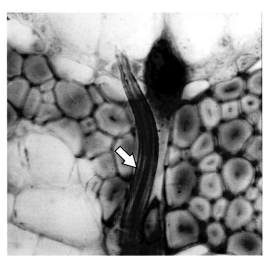

Stained cross section of a stem in which an aphid stlylet (arrow) has penetrated a sugar-conducting cell (Photo courtesy of Worth Publishers)

What are invasive plants?

Invasive plants are species that have been introduced into areas other than their natural habitats. These plants can invade natural ecosystems, agricultural areas, and forests. They often displace natural species, threaten ecosystems, and may cause major economic losses.

Invasive garlic mustard along the edge of a forest

How do invasive plant species succeed in their new environment?

Plants use various strategies to invade new areas, and often become dominant species. Plants such as spotted knapweed produce many seeds that are carried by the wind. The roots of these plants also release chemicals into the soil that are toxic to many other species, including grasses. This strategy is so effective that spotted knapweed is replacing grasslands in some prairie habitats.

Knapweed flowers

European buckthorn produces numerous fruits that are eaten by birds. Seeds pass through their digestive systems and are widely dispersed.

Fruits of European buckthorn

Some invasive species use a combination of strategies. For example, purple loosestrife and common reed grass not only produce numerous seeds but also have extensive **rhizome** systems that rapidly propagate the species.

Purple loosestrife flowers

Common reed grass

Many noxious, invasive weeds in agricultural lands spread by forming new shoots on roots so that even the smallest root piece left in the soil after cultivation can propagate the species. Examples of these species are various thistles, leafy spurge, and dandelions.

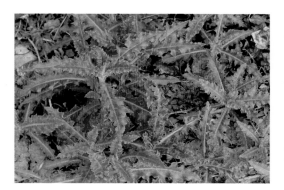
Canada thistles

Flowers of Canada thistle

Some species that have commercial uses can also become invasive under certain circumstances. A good example is sweet white clover that is used as forage for cattle and also as an important source of nectar for honey production. However, this species has become very invasive in northern North America, particularly following climate change. In the Yukon it is replacing fireweed, the territory's official flower. The numerous small seeds produced by each plant can remain viable for over 30 years.

Sweet white clover plants in flower

Are lichens plants?

Although many lichens are green, they are not plants. All lichens are a combination of an **alga** and a fungus that act symbiotically. The alga produces sugars by **photosynthesis** that are used for energy by both partners. The fungus protects the algae from environmental extremes and transports essential mineral elements to them.

Lichens on tree on Tsushima Island, Japan

How do lichens become established on tree trunks, branches, rocks, etc. ?

Small groups of algae surrounded by protective fungi break away from the lichen and are carried by wind or small animals to a new site.

Lichens on rock surface
(Photo by Irwin Brodo)

How can plants be used in solving crimes?

A field of study called Forensic Botany deals with evidence from plant material that can be used in a court of law. For example, individuals who commit crimes can accidentally pick up pieces of wood, fruits, seeds, **pollen**, plant fragments, etc. that may be linked to the scene of the crime.

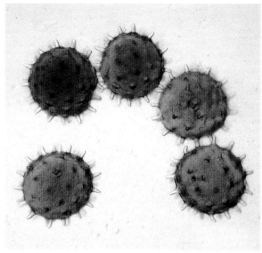

Hibiscus pollen

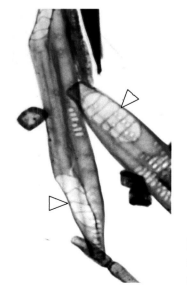

Common burdock fruits with spines that attach to clothing

Another example of Forensic Botany involves using cellular characteristics of wood in solving crimes. For example, the senior author of this book proved that flooring sold as hard maple was, in fact, birch. A critical feature was the appearance of the end walls of some water-conducting cells in the wood. Maple species always have a single opening at each end of these cells, while all birch species have a ladder-like opening at each end of these cells.

Maple water-conducting cells with open ends (arrowheads)

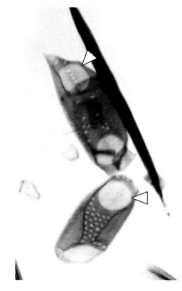

Birch water-conducting cells with ladder-like openings (arrowheads)

How are plants named?

Plants are given two scientific names, a genus name and a species name. This Latin binomial system was introduced by a Swedish botanist, Carl Linnaeus, in 1753. For example, the genus name of the common garden bean is **Phaseolus**. Its species name, **vulgaris**, means common. Species names often indicate some feature of the plant. For example, **edulis** means edible, **minor** means small, **odouratus** means fragrant, and **perennis** means perennial.

The scientific name for tobacco is **Nicotiana tabacum**. The genus refers to nicotine and the species to tobacco.

What is a herbarium?

A herbarium is a collection of dried, pressed plants that have been mounted on heavy paper. A label is attached to the paper indicating the scientific name, common name, details of the collection site, name of collector, and date of collection. Herbaria provide a permanent record of plant species and are valuable in monitoring changes in distribution of plants over time. Specimens in a herbarium also serve as reference materials for individuals needing to verify identification of species.

Plant press containing specimens for drying

Pressed, mounted, and labeled plant specimen

UNIVERSITY (OF GUELPH HERBARIUM

Trillium grandiflorum (Michaux) Salisb.

Plants of:	Ontario
Locality:	Halton Region, Milton Twp., Conc. 7, Lots 1-2 (Milton Limestone), Lat: 43,30',00", Long: 85,00',30"
Habitat:	Plateau
Remarks:	M.Sc. Thesis
Date:	June 12, 1998

(Collector No: Michele McMillan, 196
Det: J. Lundholm

Typical label for a pressed plant specimen

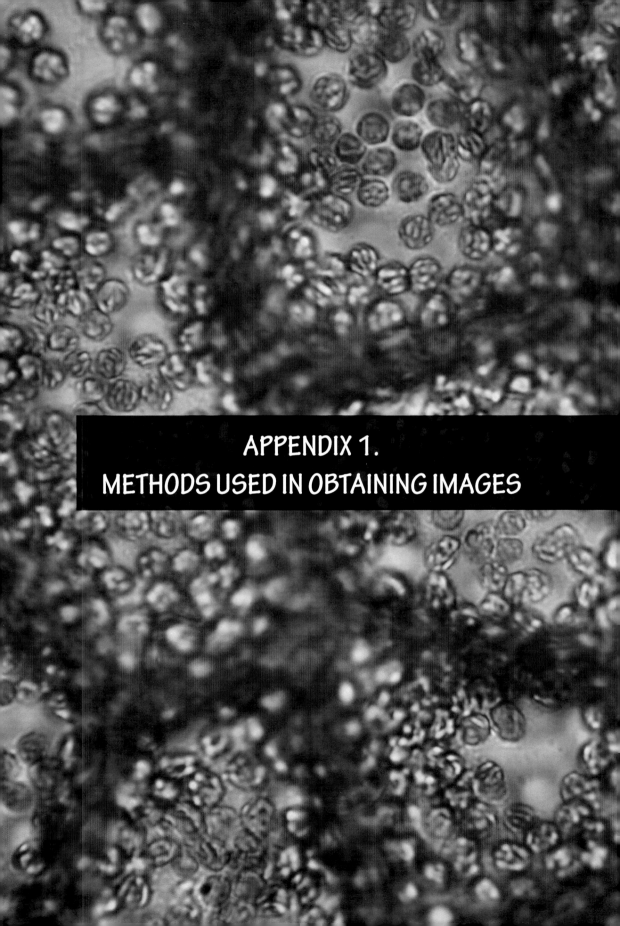

APPENDIX 1.
METHODS USED IN OBTAINING IMAGES

Appendix 1. Methods used in obtaining images

External plant features

Hand lenses

Bottom side of geranium leaf

Purple heart (***Tradescantia***) flower

Dissecting (stereobinocular) microscope This microscope is used primarily to study the external features of plants at magnifications up to 250 times.

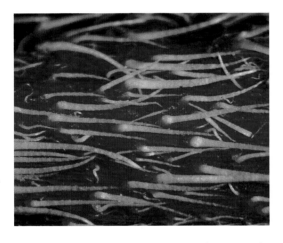

Hairs on a poppy leaf viewed with a dissecting microscope

Scanning electron microscope (SEM) This microscope is usually used to study external features of plants. Images can be obtained up to about 10,000 times magnification. Scanning electron microscopes are often used to study pollen grains, plant hairs, flower parts, and seed coats. One disadvantage of this method is that the images are in black and white so information regarding natural colour is lost.

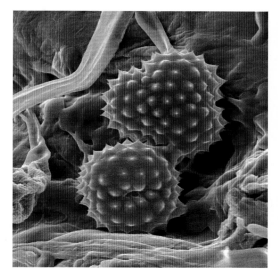

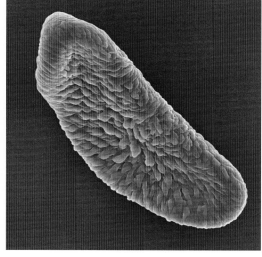

Ragweed pollen grains (SEM)   Peruvian lily pollen grain (SEM)

Internal plant features

Sectioning - Thin sections can be prepared for microscopic observation. To build a three-dimensional picture, it is necessary to make two types of sections, cross and longitudinal. Most internal structures of a plant are colourless and, therefore, sections are typically stained prior to viewing.

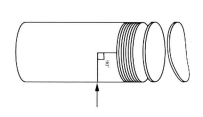

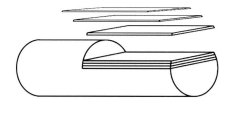

Cross sections   Longitudinal sections

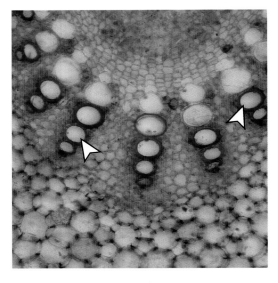

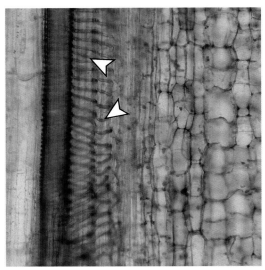

Water-conducting cells (arrowheads) in a stained cross section of sunflower stem

Water-conducting cells (arrowheads) in a stained longitudinal section of sunflower stem

Maceration Individual cells can be separated from each other by using chemicals to dissolve the substances that bind them together. This procedure is often used in studying the cells in wood.

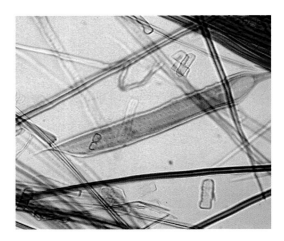

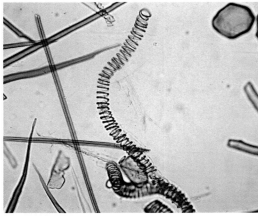

Macerated oak wood showing individual cells

Cells in macerated sunflower stem

Clearing Some organs such as leaves and petals can be treated with chemicals to dissolve most of their cellular contents, but leaving cell walls and any insoluble contents intact. This method is often used to study the patterns of veins in leaves and petals.

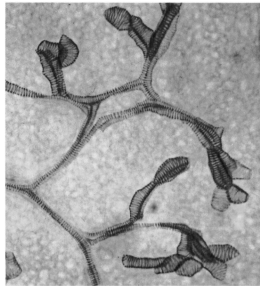

Veins in cleared poplar leaf

Veins in cleared and stained crown of thorns leaf

Polarized light microscopy This is a specialized method used for examining crystals and cell walls containing crystalline components. These structures appear bright on a black background.

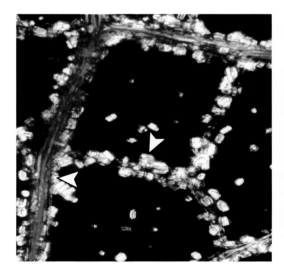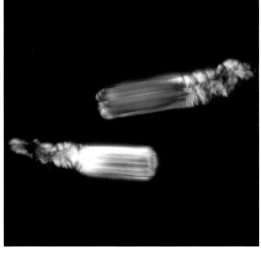

Crystals (arrowheads) mainly along veins in a cleared and stained linden tree leaf

Two cells isolated from a pea seed coat

APPENDIX 2.
COMMON AND SCIENTIFIC NAMES OF PLANTS

Appendix 2. Common and scientific names of plants

African violet (*Saintpaulia ionantha*)
alder (*Alnus* sp.)
alfalfa (*Medicago sativa*)
American basswood (*Tilia americana*)
American beech (*Fagus grandifolia*)
apple (*Malus pumila*)
asparagus (*Asparagus officinalis*)
aster (*Symphyotrichum* sp.)
avocado (*Persea americana*)
bald cypress (*Taxodium distichum*)
banana (*Musa* spp.)
barberry (*Berberis thunbergii*)
barley (*Hordeum vulgare*)
bean (*Phaseolus vulgaris*)
bee orchid (*Ophrys sicula*)
beet (*Beta vulgaris*)
begonia (*Begonia* spp.)
belladonna (*Atropa belladonna*)
birch (*Betula* spp.)
bird of paradise (*Strelitzia reginae*)
black cherry (*Prunus serotina*)
blueberry (*Vaccinium* sp.)
brome grass (*Bromus* sp.)
burdock (*Arctium minus*)
burning bush (*Euonymous alatus*)
butternut squash (*Cucurbita moschata*)
Canada thistle (*Cirsium arvense*)
canola (*Brassica napus*)
capers (*Capparis spinosa*)
carrot (*Daucus carota*)
cassava (*Manihot esculenta*)
castor bean (*Ricinus communis*)
cauliflower (*Brassica oleracea* var. *caulflora*)
celery (*Apium graveolens*)
cherries (*Prunus* spp.)
chickpea (*Cicer arietinum*)
cocoa (*Theobroma cacao*)
cocklebur (*Xanthium strumarium*)
coconut (*Cocos nucifera*)
coltsfoot (*Tussilago farfara*)
common burdock (*Arctium minus*)
common reed grass (*Phragmites australis*)

coneflower (*Echinacea angustifolia*)
cork oak (*Quercus suber*)
corn or maize (*Zea mays*)
cotton (*Gossypium* spp.)
crab apple (*Malus* sp.)
crown of thorns (*Euphorbia splendens*)
cucumber (*Cucumis sativus*)
daffodil (*Narcissus* spp.)
dandelion (*Taraxacum officinale*)
daylilies (*Hemerocallis* spp.)
deadly nightshade (*Atropa belladonna*)
dodder (*Cuscuta* spp.)
Douglas fir (*Pseudotsuga menziesii*)
duckweeds (*Lemna* spp.; *Wolffia* spp.)
dumbcane (*Dieffenbachia* sp.)
dwarf mistletoe (*Arceuthobium americanum*)
eastern prairie fringed orchid (*Platanthera leucophaea*)
eastern white cedar (*Thuja occidentalis*)
European buckthorn (*Rhamnus cathartica*)
Fairy slipper orchid (*Calypso bulbosa*)
European mistletoe (*Viscum album*)
fireweed (*Chamerion angustifolium*)
flamingo plant (*Anthurium andraenum*)
flax (*Linum usitatissimum*)
foxglove (*Digitalis purpurea*)
garden sage (*Salvia officinalis*)
garlic mustard (*Alliaria petiolata*)
geranium (*Pelargonium x hortorum*)
ghost orchid (*Dendrophylax lindonii*)
ginseng (*Panax quinquefolius*)
goldenrod (*Solidago* spp.)
grape hyacinth (*Muscari* sp.)
grape ivy (*Rhoicissus rhomboidea*)
grapes (*Vitis* spp.)
ground pine (*Lycopodium* spp.; *Lycopodiella* spp.; *Diphasiastrum* spp.)
hawkweed (*Hieracium* sp.)
hemp (*Cannabis sativa*)
hibiscus (*Hibiscus* spp.)
horse chestnut (*Aesculus hippocastanum*)
horsetails (*Equisetum* spp.)
Indian pipe (*Monotropa uniflora*)
ivy (*Hedera* sp.)
Japanese maple (*Acer palmatum*)
Jimsonweed (*Datura stramonium*)
knapweed (*Centaurea* spp.)

leek (*Allium porrum*)
lemons (*Citrus limon*)
lentils (*Lens culinaris*)
lettuce (*Lactuca sativa*)
lilac (*Syringa vulgaris*)
limes (*Citrus aurantifolia*)
linden (*Tilia americana*)
lupin (*Lupinus polyphyllus*)
Madagascar periwinkle (*Catharanthus roseus* = *Vinca rosea*)
mangrove (*Rhizophora* sp.)
manioc (*Manihot esculenta*)
maple (*Acer* spp.)
marigold (*Tagetes erecta*)
marijuana (*Cannabis sativa*)
marsh marigold (*Caltha palustris*)
milkweed (*Asclepias syriaca*)
mints (*Mentha* spp.)
monkey puzzle trees (*Araucaria* spp.)
mullein (*Verbascum thapsus*)
Norway maple (*Acer platanoides*)
oak (*Quercus* spp.)
old man cactus (*Cephalocereus senilis*)
onion (*Allium cepa*)
opium poppy (*Papaver somniferum*)
oranges (*Citrus sinensis*)
ostrich fern (*Matteuccia struthiopteris*)
Pacific yew (*Taxus brevifolia*)
pansy (*Viola* spp.)
parsley (*Petroselinum crispum*)
pawpaw (*Asiminia triloba*)
pea (*Pisum sativum*)
peanut (*Arachis hypogea*)
pear (*Pyrus communis*)
peppers (*Capsicum annuum*)
Peruvian lily (*Alstroemeria aurea*)
petunias (*Petunia* spp.)
pine (*Pinus* spp.)
pineapple (*Ananas comosus*)
pitcher plants (*Nepenthes* spp.; *Sarracenia* spp.)
plums (*Prunus domestica*)
poinsettia (*Euphorbia pulcherrima*)
poison ivy (*Toxicodendron radicans*)
poplar (*Populus* sp.)
poppy (*Papaver somniferum*)
potato (*Solanum tuberosum*)

prayer plant (*Maranta leuconeura*)
purple-heart tradescantia (*Tradescantia pallida*)
purple loosesrife (*Lythrum salicaria*)
pussy willow (*Salix discolor*)
ragweed (*Ambrosia artemisiifolia*)
raspberry (*Rubus idaeus*)
red cedar (*Thuja plicata*)
red maple (*Acer rubrum*)
red tingle Eucalyptus (*Eucalyptus jacksonii*)
redwood (*Sequoia sempervirens*)
rice (*Oryza sativa*)
roses (*Rosa* spp.)
rubber tree (*Hevea brasiliensis*)
saffron crocus (*Crocus sativus*)
sage (*Salvia officinalis*)
scarlet bee balm (*Monarda didyma*)
scarlet runner bean (*Phaseolus coccineus*)
Scots pine (*Pinus sylvestris*)
sedum (*Sedum* spp.)
Shasta daisy (*Leucanthemum x superbum*)
showy lady's slipper orchid (*Cypripedium reginae*)
silver maple (*Acer saccharinum*)
snapdragon (*Antirrhinum majus*)
snow plant (*Sarcodes sanguinea*)
soybean (*Glycine max*)
splitleaf philodendron (*Monstera delisiosa*)
spruce (*Picea* spp.)
squash (*Cucurbita* spp.)
staghorn sumac (*Rhus typhina*)
stinging nettle (*Urtica dioica*)
Sturt's desert pea (*Swainsona formosa*)
sugar maple (*Acer saccharum*)
sunflower (*Helianthus annuus*)
sweet potato (*Ipomoea batatas*)
sweet white clover (*Melilotus alba*)
sweet Willam (*Dianthus barbatus*)
Titan arum (*Amorphophallus titanum*)
tobacco (*Nicotiana tabacum*)
tomato (*Solanum lycopersicum*)
tulip (*Tulipa gesneriana*)
tulip tree (*Liriodendron tulipifera*)
umbrella tree (*Schefflera actinophylla*)
vanilla orchid (*Vanilla planifolia*)
velvet plant (*Gynura aurantiaca*)
Venus flytrap (*Dionaea muscipula*)

wheat (*Triticum aestivum*)
white birch (*Betula papyrifera*)
white mustard (*Sinapis alba*)
white pine (*Pinus strobus*)
wild blue flax (*Linum lewisii*)
wild grape (*Vitis vinifera*)
willow (*Salix* spp.)
yams (*Dioscorea* spp.)
yellow birch (*Betula alleghaniensis*)
yellow lady slipper orchid (*Cypripedium pubescens* var. *pubescens*)
yew (*Taxus* sp.)
yucca (*Yucca* sp.)

GLOSSARY

Photo by Günter Gerlach

Glossary

aerial root: a root that grows above ground.

alga (pl. algae): a diverse group of typically aquatic organisms ranging from single-celled, green individuals to large brown and red seaweeds.

alkaloid: a complex molecule composed of nitrogen, hydrogen, carbon and sometimes oxygen and other elements. Some alkaloids are toxic at high doses. Some examples of alkaloids are atropine, caffeine, cocaine, morphine, quinine, and solanine.

angiosperms: plants that reproduce by means of flowers.

annual ring: in a cross section of wood, a ring consisting of a layer of lighter early wood and darker late wood comprising the wood produced in one growing season.

anther: the part of a stamen (the male part of a flower) that produces pollen.

anthocyanin: a red, blue or purple pigment found in cell vacuoles. When in the epidermis, functions to absorb excess light radiation that could be harmful to the plant. When found in petals it provides colours attractive to insects.

apical meristem: a region of dividing cells located at the tip of an organ, e.g. stem, root.

atropine: a naturally occurring alkaloid found in Jimson weed.

bark: the part of stems and roots external to the wood in woody plants.

betacyanin: a reddish to violet pigment located in the vacuoles of cells such as those of beet roots.

bud: an embryonic shoot or flower.

cambium: a row of cells that divide, producing new cells on one or both sides of the row; usually refers to vascular cambium or cork cambium.

carotene: an orange pigment that occurs in small amounts in chloroplasts and in large amounts in chromoplasts.

carotenoid: a general term that includes orange and yellow pigments such as carotene and xanthophyll.

carpel: the female part of a flower consisting of stigma, style and ovary.

cell wall: a complex structure that encloses a plant cell. Its major components are cellulose, pectic substances, proteins, water and, in some cells lignin or suberin.

cellulose: a major component of cell walls. A molecule of cellulose is an unbranched chain of glucose molecules.

cereals: edible grain species belonging to the grass family.

chlorophyll: a green pigment located in chloroplasts. As a complex with proteins, it absorbs light for photosynthesis.

chloroplast: a green, chlorophyll-containing plastid, capable of photosynthesis.

chromoplast: a type of plastid that is a colour other than green.

cork: the outer protective region of woody stems that consists of cells with suberin and wax in their walls.

cork cambium: a layer or arcs of cells that form the cork tissue in woody stems and roots.

condensed tannins: highly complex molecules that have antibacterial and antifungal properties; often found in the walls of cork cells.

cotyledons: parts of an embryo that often store food for the future growth of the embryo during germination, and growth of the young seedling.

cuticle: a thin layer composed of cutin and wax (hydrophobic substances) that covers plant stems and leaves, preventing excessive water loss.

cutin: a hydrophobic compound that is found in the cuticle.

dormancy: a condition in seeds and other plant organs in which growth is arrested.

duct: within a plant, a long tube lined with secretory cells. The center of the duct may contain resins, latex or other compounds.

embryo: a young plant within a seed.

endosperm: a part of a seed in which food is stored, usually in the form of oil or starch.

epidermis: the outermost cell layer of the plant (except in older stems and roots of woody plants).

epiphyte: a non-parasitic plant that grows on another plant. An adaptation that allows a plant to live high in a canopy.

fertilization: in plants, the fusion of a sperm cell with an egg cell in flowers.

fibers: elongated cells with pointed ends that have thick, lignified walls and are dead at maturity. They function to support the plant.

fruit: a seed-containing structure developed from an ovary within a flower.

gall: an abnormal growth that results from an insect invasion of a plant.

gametophyte: a plant or plant part composed of cells with one set of chromosomes.

germination: the emergence of a growing embryo from a seed.

gland: a somewhat spherical, open region of the plant into which substances are secreted.

guard cells: pairs of cells in the shoot epidermis that create an opening (pore) to allow gas exchange for photosynthesis.

hair: an outgrowth of a single epidermal cell to form a single celled or multicellular structure that protrudes from the plant surface.

hardwood: wood consisting of primitive and advanced water-conducting cells along with many fibers; characteristic of flowering trees.

haustoria: specialized structures formed by a parasitic plant for the purpose of absorbing food from another plant.

heartwood: the oldest part of the wood, located centrally in a tree. This wood has ceased to function in long distance transport of water and minerals but still plays an important role in mechanical support of the tree. It may be darker in colour than the sapwood due to the presence of condensed tannins.

histamine: a nitrogen-containing compound that causes local immune responses.

honeydew: sugary droplets emanating from aphids that are feeding on the contents of sugar-conducting cells.

hormone: a substance that, when present even in a very small amount, will have a profound impact on plant growth and/or development.

hypha (pl. hyphae): a thread-like cell or group of cells in tandem that make up the bodies of fungi.

inflorescence: a group of flowers produced from the same apical (flowering) meristem.

kernel: a type of fruit that has one seed, and in which the seed coat has fused with the fruit wall; produced by corn (maize), wheat, barley and other grasses.

latex: a milky substance that, in the rubber tree, is the source of natural rubber.

laticifer: an elongate cell or a group of cells in tandem that produces latex within the plant.

leaf blade: a leaf part that is usually flattened and is adapted for catching sunlight. (The other part of the leaf is the petiole.)

lenticel: a structure in the bark of woody plants in which the cells are not tightly packed together, allowing for gas exchange between the plant and the atmosphere.

leucoplast: a colourless plastid.

lignin: a polymer of phenolic substances that forms within the walls of some cells, making them very strong.

lipids: substances such as fats and oils.

lycopene: a red, fat-soluble pigment found in fruits of tomato, papaya, watermelon, and pink grapefruit.

mycelium: a group of fungal hyphae.

mycorrhiza: a symbiotic relationship between a plant root and a soil fungus.

nectar: a solution of sugars and amino acids secreted by flowers to attract and reward pollinating insects.

nectary: a group of cells that produce and secrete nectar; located within or near flowers.

nodule: a swollen area on a plant root that contains bacteria that convert atmospheric nitrogen to a form useful to plants; a common feature of legumes.

oil gland: an internal structure that synthesizes and stores oils.

outer bark: the dead part of the bark in older trees.

ovary: in a flower, part of a carpel or fused carpels containing one or more ovules. Following fertilization of the ovules, the ovary develops into a fruit.

ovules: small spherical structures located in the ovary of a flower. Following fertilization, an ovule develops into a seed.

pectic substances (pectins): a component of the cell wall. They are located within the cell wall along with the cellulose, but also occur in higher concentration toward the outer edge of the wall, forming the "glue" that holds the cells together.

petiole: the stalk-like part of a leaf that attaches it to the stem.

photosynthesis: a complex biochemical process whereby plants synthesize carbohydrates from carbon dioxide and water, and emit oxygen gas.

phytochrome: a pigment that absorbs light and is involved in the control of flowering in some plant species.

plastid: an organelle located in the cytoplasm of plant cells; see chloroplast, chromoplast, leucoplast.

pollen: a small, tough-walled structure that contains the sperm of the plant.

pollen tube: an elongated structure (formed by a pollen grain) that delivers a sperm cell to the egg.

pollination: the transfer of pollen from one flower to another either by wind or various animals.

protein: a polymer of amino acids.

resin: a sticky substance produced in ducts of some trees (especially pine); it seals injured areas of the plant, preventing the invasion of pathogens.

resin duct: a long tube within a plant (e.g. pine) into which the peripheral cells adjacent to it secrete resin.

retting: an ancient process whereby lignified cells (especially fibers) are separated from the rest of the plant or plant part by soaking it in water and allowing it to rot. Lignified cell walls are more resistant to bacterial degradation than non-lignified walls.

rhizome: an underground stem.

root cap: a protective structure at the tip of a root; its cells are continuously shed and are replaced by the root apical meristem.

root hair: an elongated, single epidermal cell in roots; important in taking up ions and water from the soil.

root nodule: a swollen area on a root that has been colonized by nitrogen-fixing bacteria. The nodule provides a low-oxygen environment required by the bacteria to incorporate atmospheric nitrogen into carbon compounds.

salicylic acid: the active ingredient in aspirin.

sapwood: the youngest wood, closest to the outside of a tree; functions in long distance transport of water and minerals in woody plants.

seed coat: the outer protective layer(s) of a seed.

softwood: wood consisting of simple water-conducting cells and few fibers; characteristic of conifers.

spadix: a spike-like fleshy structure with many small flowers.

spathe: a modified, petal-like leaf.

sporangia: structures that produce spores.

spore: a one-celled reproductive structure.

stamen: the male part of a flower that produces pollen.

starch: a polymer of glucose molecules; one of the main forms of food storage in plants.

stigma: the upper end of a carpel; receives the pollen grains.

stoma (pl. stomata): a pore surrounded by a pair of guard cells in the leaf and young stem epidermis.

stone cell: a small, tough, dead cell with very thick, lignified walls.

style: part of a carpel or carpels of a flower; connects the stigma and ovary.

suberin: a somewhat hydrophobic polymer of phenols and fatty acids associated with the walls of some plant cells (e.g. cork). It functions to protect the plant from pathogens and, in combination with wax layers, protects the stems of woody plants from water loss.

tannins: highly complex molecules that have antibacterial and antifungal properties.

tuber: a swollen stem in which food is stored for the plant (e.g. potato).

urushiol: an oily compound found in plants such as poison ivy; often causes allergic reactions.

vacuole: a large compartment in a typical plant cell; contains water and waste products; surrounded by the cytoplasm and separated from it by a membrane.

vascular cambium: a layer of dividing cells that produces derivatives toward the inside and also toward the outside of the stem or root. The former mature into wood; the latter mature into sugar-conducting tissue.

velamen: a specialized multilayered epidermis found in aerial roots of orchids.

wax: the most hydrophobic chemical made by plants; a component of the cuticle.

wood: water-conducting and supporting tissue formed in trees and bushes.

xanthophyll: a yellow pigment located in plant chloroplasts; it becomes more abundant in fall, contributing to a colour change in leaves.